HAMMER, SI

GULARA VINCENT

HAMMER, SICKLE & BROOM

*A Memoir of Intergenerational Trauma
in Azerbaijan*

First published in 2021 by Fuzzy Flamingo
www.fuzzyflamingo.co.uk

ISBN: 978-1-8384388-4-5

Cover design and typesetting: Fuzzy Flamingo
www.fuzzyflamingo.co.uk

Back cover photograph by Khalid Zeynalov
https://instagram.com/khalidzeynalov

To Caspian and Jasmin

CONTENTS

	Acknowledgements	ix
1	Where Black Rivers Meet	1
2	Opportunities	13
3	Pioneer	26
4	A Change of Destination	37
5	Celebration	52
6	News	65
7	Victory Day	78
8	Return	88
9	Sugar Lumps	103
10	Music	118
11	Cursed	125
12	Absence	135
13	Farewell	149
14	Crystal Rain	169
15	Black January	187
16	Waiting…	203
17	It Was All a Lie!	213
18	Choices	227
19	Whiskers of a Tiger	246
	About the Author	259

ACKNOWLEDGEMENTS

I wrote this book to make sense of my life, but somewhere on this journey I fell in love with writing and telling my story became non-negotiable. My soul wanted me to write.

It has been a decade-long journey and I have many people and organisations to thank for making this dream a reality. Some of those influences had an impact before I even conceived of becoming an author.

I have deep gratitude for:

- John and Rose Ann Porter, who saw my potential and enabled my growth while I worked for the American Bar Association in Azerbaijan;
- The British Council who made it possible for me to do my Master's Degree in the UK and the University of Birmingham for funding my PhD programme;
- Writing West Midlands who accepted me as a writer before I did;
- My friend Kush who knows all my stories and still loves me;
- Ali Stubbs who provided invaluable editorial support;
- My wider healing and writing community who have been a constant source of encouragement;

- My brother and sister who have never stopped believing in me;
- My grandmother who always loved me and in her strange way encouraged me to aspire to freedom;
- And many other people along the way who have influenced me, who have helped me to heal, and who stood by me as I worked on my memoir.

Finally, I want to thank my two dear children who have been patiently by my side, while I juggled motherhood, university lectureship, writing this book and building a healing practice. My prayer is that the suffering I have endured as a child stops with me.

'A woman is like a broom;
she should stay where you put her.'

Unknown

WHERE BLACK RIVERS MEET

Kirovabad, Azerbaijan Soviet Socialist Republic, 1981

S he stood in front of the kitchen door. Silent. I tried to see past her. Why was she acting so strangely? The answer was behind her and I wanted to see what it was, no matter what.

'Mama, you okay?'

'Go play.'

She sounded tired. I tried to go into the kitchen, but her body blocked the doorframe, her arms behind her back. I dropped down and peered between her legs at the kitchen floor. Two puddles of dark liquid pooled on the wooden floorboards. Had Mama cut a chicken? It could not be that because that was Uncle Salman's job. Besides, they were always cut outdoors.

My eyes sought other clues for Mama's behaviour. The bare legs of the square kitchen table, Nana's old wooden chair where she always sat to prepare food, a china sink with rusty pipes and the ever busy, white gas cooker – they were all the same, but Mama was not.

I stood up and stared at Mama as she staggered to flop down in the chair facing the open door. A network of small black rivers ran down from her wrists. Some looked dry, almost old; others tightly hugged the curve of her short fingers. The trails were thick and dark. Long slits gaped open on her wrists. I screamed as Mama hugged her arms into her floral cotton dress.

'What is it?' Nana's voice croaked from the other room behind me. 'Is it a snake?' Her heavy footsteps were rapidly approaching me. 'Maryam! What have you done?'

She swooped towards Mama, cradled her in shaking arms and shrieked: 'Ali! Come quickly. No, call an ambulance first! Bring bandages. For Allah's sake, hurry.'

I watched her stroking Mama's hair, covering her head with kisses.

'Hurry, hurry. I will not lose another child.'

Baba brushed past me as I stood mesmerised against the wall. He scooped Mama up into his arms.

'What's happening?' shouted Uncle Telman, emerging from the drawing room to join us, as we followed Baba carrying Mama to the sky-blue front gates. The blood told it all.

'She has tried it again? Even after Javan?' His jaw tensed as his right hand curled into a tight fist.

'Damn that man,' Nana gasped as she stumbled on. Who did she mean? My heart was drumming, my tummy twisting, as I tried to keep pace with them.

Nana choked on a sob and moved faster, turning her face away from us. I alone knew she cried over Uncle Javan's photo when the others were out. He'd been stabbed to death three years before I was born. I alone knew she had taken to secret smoking, as she said, to numb the pain. I had sat in the shameful, sinful fug as she talked and

2

worried. She was the centre of my world. As she rushed weeping to where Baba held Mama by the garden gates, I followed, confused but sobbing too.

Baba's loving embrace of Mama seemed strange. I could not remember him showing any affection to her before. I could only see his silver hair from where I stood but I wished I could see his expression. He shifted from foot to foot until Uncle Telman opened the gate.

Our street, named after the Soviet hero Chiragidzor, was quiet. No people, no cars. Two rows of houses, each unique in their design and size, stood facing each other while my grandparents put Mama on the spacious back seat of Baba's battered beige beetle-shaped car. Red-bricked walls, tall iron gates and tiled roofs glistened in the morning sun, as the car revved, and Nana scurried to sit next to Mama. She was still wearing the new house *khalat* she had made for herself, its roses now smeared with blood.

I stepped towards the car, hoping to go along, but Uncle Telman's heavy hand landed on my shoulder. We watched the car speed away, raising a cloud of dust, until it was out of sight, before returning to the house where my uncle locked himself in the kitchen.

★★★

As the day progressed, I felt increasingly restless. I tried to hit the keys on an old piano to play a tune Mama taught me, but it made me too sad. I roamed the living room, taking turns to sit on a hard sofa, then on an armchair, staring at a blank screen of a black and white TV on a sideboard. Mama's vinyl player, which she kept pristine and usually unused, looked forlorn in the corner. When Uncle Telman made clattering noises in the kitchen, I migrated to a large oval table covered with a plastic tablecloth, pretending to drink a glass of compote left unfinished. After some time, I retired to the bedroom I shared with Mama. It felt empty and cold without her.

Would they make it home before bedtime?

I loved the way she would scratch my back to comfort me and sing a little lullaby. I laid myself down on her bed remembering then, listening to the heavy silence, only punctuated by an occasional vehicle passing down the road.

Much later, as the honeysuckle-scented, purple dusk began to fall, I heard a car door bang outside. A plaintive creak of the iron gate announced that someone was coming in. Springing to my feet, I peered out of the window into the front garden. Through the persimmon tree's leafy branches, I glimpsed first Nana's square set frame, then Baba's, leading Mama between the receding rays of the setting sun.

I sprinted down the stone stairs into the front garden, hoping for a welcome home hug but drew back when I saw Mama's two cousins were also there. With eyebrows furrowed and lips pursed with concern, their cold, dark brown eyes seemed to say, 'do not approach'. They were dressed in similar Turkish-coffee-coloured skirts and taupe shirts, which made their complexion even darker. While they marched towards the entrance door, I wondered whether someone like Nana made their outfits.

Barely acknowledging me, the procession entered the house. I hesitated a moment, and then followed them. Nana helped Mama into bed and tucked her in. Mama looked resigned; pale and tired, she avoided eye contact with me.

Chairs were arranged by the bed, facing a low dressing table with a tall mirror, fitted neatly between two large windows. Heads were bowed in silent contemplation. Ignored, I stood at the foot of the bed wanting to be closer to Mama, to hold her. I wanted to know why, why did she want to leave me? Would she try it again? With the silence in the room growing taut as a stretched elastic band, I left to sit on the cold stone stairs outside, alone.

Relatives trickled in, brief greetings were exchanged, before I directed them to the bedroom. Soon, the stairs were crowded with shoes.

Attempting to block out the too-loud hushed voices and intermittent moaning, I turned my attention to examining the piled footwear. Some shoes were coated with the dust of our street whilst others were smothered in unfamiliar, once wet, now dried mud. I recognised the stiff black galoshes of Nana's nearest friend, a hairy-chinned woman who had lots to say about what a six-year-old girl should wear and know. Relatives and friends who had travelled from other parts of the city had come in more formal shoes. Like most of their owners, the men's shoes seemed ominously serious and heavy, cut as they were from stiff, black leather, with sturdy heels.

The women's shoes looked far less practical, made of softer leathers and dyed shades of brown and beige. The stones and uneven road surfaces had marked them. Those dented at the toes had to be the oldest. Only two pairs were black. One of these was Mama's and her shoes were definitely the finest. I picked up the black, shiny shoes, with high heels and a thin buckle, which usually hugged her ankles.

I had been with her when she bought them. The vendor had flattered her, saying that fine feet deserved fine shoes. Now I could see that there was a trace of mud on the bottom. Fetching an old rag and a pot of water, I carefully started to clean, first her shoes, then twenty other pairs. The monotony of picking up each shoe and giving it a good clean focused me; I was absorbed in the task because it made me feel useful.

'Gulush, what are you doing?' Mirza *Dayi,* our neighbour, called out to me. I did not like my nickname at home, especially today, because I did not live up to its meaning: 'laughter'. He was staring at me. I did not know how long he had been standing in the doorway. His greying curly hair looked like a fluffy cloud around his head. I hastily wiped my tears off and attempted a smile.

'Just trying to tidy up,' I said.

'Don't bother cleaning my shoes. You should come inside.'

'In a minute,' I said, without meaning it.

After a while, the visitors started leaving. Shoes disappeared from the stairs without comment and, at last, it was just us.

'You'll sleep with us tonight,' Nana said as soon as I entered Mama's bedroom. I knew what that meant. I had spent many nights sleeping in the coffin-wide gap between their two single beds. Nana stuffed it with old blankets, but it was still uncomfortable. Baba might snore and keep me awake but Nana would always tell me off if I moved a muscle.

'You know if I wake up, I can't fall asleep,' she reminded me, even before we went to bed. 'So, no fidgeting, do you hear me?'

There was no point in objecting, but I worried about Mama. What if she decided to do something 'stupid' again? She would not be able to say goodbye if I was not there. I wanted to stay with her, to guard her, to talk to her and say it was going to be all right.

Later that night, laying wide awake between my snoring grandparents, I tried to work out who Nana meant when she cursed 'that man'. It had to be Avaz.

I liked Avaz. He was tall with soft, round features, a warm smile, and short black hair. Mama took me for walks with him on weekends. I was not allowed to say how they met in a deserted park and strolled hand in hand. When we were out together, he often bought me ice cream and a ticket to race on the dodgems. Whilst I crashed about with the electrical cables spitting sparks above me, I could see him and Mama sitting and talking. Sometimes they would wave at me.

I wanted them to get married because I knew that meeting secretly was not right. Nana said a good marriage was by far the most important thing in a woman's life. It made a woman respectable, even loved, sometimes.

'Mama, why aren't you married?' I had asked her a few weeks ago, when we were looking at the rolls of bright fabric, large crystal vases and chandeliers displayed in the vast windows of the *Univermag*. Although I knew she and my father were divorced, we never talked about him. It was not that I was told off for mentioning him, I just never did. Perhaps even as a child, I sensed that dwelling on the past might be painful.

Mama had smiled at my question. 'Do you want me to marry?'

'Yes, you're so beautiful and I haven't told anyone you yell at me, honest!'

I hoped she would tell me she'd marry soon. We'd all live together in a big house with an indoor toilet, with fine things from *Alverchi*, just like the Communist Party officials. She laughed heartily, but although she recounted our conversation to all her friends, she had kept her relationship a secret, until someone saw them and told Baba.

Then she was in terrible trouble. Baba was very angry when he came home from work. He shouted at Nana, using heavy, ugly swearwords. It made me want to cry. Baba was scary when he was nice, never mind when he was cross. Now, here he was, right next to me, snoring noisily. I squirmed away from him, trying to push the memory away, but it persisted, and I continued replaying it in my mind's eye.

'Telman,' Baba had raged, 'you will have to beat some sense into your sister. She has been disgracing us all with her behaviour. If I get hold of her, she'll soon be dead.'

My heart had raced listening to Baba's voice. I had overheard stories of his strictness before. He even smashed Mama's head on the wall once, when he thought she was seeing someone. This was not an empty threat, to kill Mama.

I remembered how I hid in the drawing room, frozen. When Baba had left the adjacent living room, I shook with relief, but Nana started telling Uncle Telman everything.

'A friend called your father to say he had seen them sneaking into an empty building. Your dad drove there but they were gone already, lucky! If he had walked in on them who knows what might have happened! If she carries on like this, she'll ruin her own life and get one of you into trouble as well. Your dad would have killed that guy today, and possibly her too. You must teach her a lesson. People worship me for my purity and morals, so I don't know who she takes after. Lusting for…'

'All right. Enough,' said Uncle Telman. Through a crack in the door, I saw how he flexed his muscular arms and went to the lobby, which opened into Mama's bedroom. Motionless, I listened to Uncle Telman's stern voice.

'Maryam! Come here immediately!'

Time stopped. Silence. A dreadful pause.

Thump.

'You have to stop this behaviour, Maryam! You are bringing shame on all of us!'

Thump.

I thought I heard whimpering. I tiptoed into the living room and opened the door into a small rectangular lobby that led to the staircase.

Thump.

She was crouching on the floor, on the left side of the lobby. Pressing her head between her knees, she guarded it with her arms. Uncle Telman was normally nice to me, but not today.

'Get out of here,' he said, while I backed out of the lobby into the living room.

The memory of that horrible day felt like a punch in my tummy. Upset, as if it all happened today, I cried myself to sleep.

★★★

Next morning, I wriggled past Nana the first chance I got to find that Mama was still very much alive, though ivory pale with fatigue.

'Good morning, Mama.'

I skipped towards her, while Nana started laying the breakfast in front of Mama on the large oval table in the living room. I noticed honey with small chunks of honeycomb, and thick clotted cream: the hallmarks of a special occasion.

'You're not going to work?' I asked.

I imagined how wonderful it would be to spend some time with her.

She pecked me on my forehead. I waited for an answer, for some acknowledgement of what had happened that night, to hear about the hospital and what might come next, but instead, we ate in unbroken silence.

The rest of the day, though I strained my ears to hear what the adults were talking about, I did not hear a single reference to Mama's condition or our future. Subdued, Nana seemed to forget to send me to kindergarten, but I did not mind and kept out of the adults' way.

The next day was the same, with Nana being nice to Mama. I was playing in the garden alone, enjoying the gentle warmth of late spring sun, when something in Uncle Telman's voice drew me closer to the open window of the drawing room.

'It serves her right, Sevil,' he was saying on the phone. 'We've warned her several times.'

He must have been speaking about Mama to Sevil, his secret girlfriend. He kept his relationship private from my grandparents, but not from the rest of us.

'Avaz is the only child in the family, and he's three years

younger than her. What does she expect from him? He's only twenty-three. Of course, his family will oppose this marriage. Mine would do too.' He paused, but before I could tiptoe away, he spoke again, choking on his frustration. 'No, it's not the same, Sevil, you and I are both twenty-one and you are not, you know... Surely, she understands that his parents didn't raise a son to have him marry a divorcee with a child.'

I walked away from his hurtful voice and perched on a step in the shade of the blossoming persimmon tree. Even the sight of its first small bell-shaped cream-coloured flowers could not distract me from worrying about Mama's future.

★★★

As soon as Mama's wrists healed, she resumed her job as a music teacher and life went back to 'normal'. Nana no longer was kind or loving and Mama annoyed her with her attitude.

'You'll get meningitis,' Nana said. 'You shouldn't leave for work with wet hair.'

Mama took no notice. She had black locks cascading all the way to her waist and sat in front of a tall mirror in our shared bedroom. I drew closer, to breathe in the comforting scent of her egg yolk shampoo, which I preferred to Nana's, which smelt of stately pine trees.

'Can I comb your hair?' I asked.

'No, it irritates me. Besides, I don't have time. I may be late for work.'

She took a jar of facial cream from a cabinet drawer,

dipped in her middle fingers and dotted the mixture on her sculptured cheekbones before rubbing it in with circular motions. Admiring her in the mirror, I noted how different we looked. Presumably, my grey-blue eyes, fair skin and chestnut hair had to constantly remind her of my dad.

Nana startled me as she barged into the room with a pile of ironed linen.

'You are going to ruin your skin. Look at mine,' Nana said, 'nothing ever touched my face and it's smooth as marble.'

'What do you know about it? You come from a backward generation,' Mama said.

'And what have you achieved by being progressive? Brought shame on all the family.'

I knew this dialogue by heart. It upset my tummy when they said hurtful things to each other. Unable to stop them, and in case I was swept up in the crossfire, I sneaked out of the room. When I ventured back several minutes later, they were still squabbling.

'And what is that? Mascara? And eyeliner too? Didn't your dad throw them down the toilet last week? You couldn't possibly have retrieved them from that hole.'

'Right. Enough. I'm leaving!' Mama gathered her cosmetics into a bag and smoothed down her long white dress with small grey flower patterns.

'Aren't you going to eat before you go? I prepared your breakfast an hour ago,' Nana said through gritted teeth, breathless with rage.

'No, you've poisoned me enough for one day,' said Mama as she went downstairs, put on her shoes, and left.

The sound of her high heels stabbed the silence.

2.

OPPORTUNITIES

Kirovabad, Azerbaijan S.S.R., 1982

I clasped Mama's soft hand as we walked out of the school gate. A slight wind ruffled her black wavy hair, which flowed down her back. She took my schoolbag from me, then nudged me to turn left. This was not our usual route home and I wondered whether Mama was planning to take me to the park, which we had not visited since she cut her wrists. Was she back with Avaz? I missed seeing him, but the thought of them resuming their secret relationship made my innards freeze.

A silky breeze caressed my forearms and soothed my brow. I drank in the warmth of the early autumn air, which had finally replaced the unbearable heat of a boring summer. The streets around the school were quiet, dotted with other parents leading first year pupils from my school. I waved at another seven-year-old girl from my class peering from the back seat of her dad's car as they whizzed by.

We marched into the city centre with busy shops and noisy traffic. Older men and some women bustled around us purposefully, unlike my neighbourhood where not many people had jobs, smoking cheap stinky cigarettes on the street corners and littering the ground with their stubbed out stumps.

When she walked the opposite way to the park, I finally asked: 'Where are we going?'

'To see my new workplace,' she said, her dark eyes shining like sunrise.

She was a piano teacher, and I loved our second-hand piano, with its gold hand-painted decorations, made in Leipzig. Baba was proud of the bargain he'd struck for it. I knew all the notes and when Mama's fingers ran over the keys, I felt mesmerised by its mellow tone. As I followed Mama I wondered if her new workplace would have more pianos for me to try.

We stopped outside a majestic two-storey building. Mama opened the huge, studded door and we climbed a wide marble staircase that led into a spacious hall. Our footsteps echoed in its high vaulted ceiling. This was nothing like our current music school and I was hushed by its grandeur. It looked very old. Through an open door I glimpsed long rows of cabinets, the nearest filled with sparkling jewellery and colourful, but broken, pots.

Confused, I tugged at the sleeve of Mama's black dress.

'Is it a museum?' I whispered.

'Yes, and I'm its new temporary director!' she replied as she hugged me.

Because this was a public space, I had to suppress my desire to whoop and twirl her round to celebrate, so I just giggled.

I wanted to ask what temporary meant but knew to keep silent as Mama greeted several older women who worked there. She introduced me and they all cooed, saying they could not believe she had a seven-year-old daughter, since she looked so young herself.

I did not discover how she'd got such a job until we were alone in the park later.

'A friend heard about the job and Nana helped smooth the way with a donation to the Museum fund.'

That was called a bribe, I knew that. Uncle Telman often said 'that is how things are done here' when discussing his job prospects.

Thoughtful, I walked the length of the bench, jumped and landed like a monkey.

'What is tempour-rare-ray?' I asked carefully.

Mama laughed.

'Temporary means not forever. Directors are usually men, but they couldn't find one that was willing to pay to get the job. So, I am Director until they do.'

'Then you'll lose your job?' I felt anxious.

'No, I'll be his deputy.'

★★★

The museum had fascinated me. I wanted to know all about it. As we walked around the park, Mama told me that the splendid building had actually once been someone's house.

'It belonged to the last *Khan* of Ganja and his family for about 200 years,' she explained.

'What's Ganja?'

'That's what our city used to be called and *Khan* was a ruler.'

'Shouldn't the house have crumbled by now?' I asked.

The *Khan* must have had such a large family, I thought, to fill all the space, with thick rich carpets, soft pillows and many other beautiful things. Then I shivered. 'Did the *Khan* die there?'

'No, silly. He died in a battle against the Russians,' Mama replied. 'But others did die.' She frowned. 'I'm not sure I should tell you everything.'

'I am seven!' I protested.

She drew in a breath. 'Very well, my petal. During a war with Russia two centuries ago, Ganja was under siege. General Tsitsianov approached Javad *Khan* and asked him to submit to the Russian rule. The *Khan* and his army chose to fight to protect the city from invasion. In the thick of the night, some Armenians residing in the city opened the gates of the castle and let the Russians in. That day, Javad *Khan* and his sons were killed in a battle.'

I was so proud of Mama, that she knew history so well, but I wondered where she had learnt it. Would they tell me all this in my new school?

'This building belonged to the family of the *Khan* until recently. When Azerbaijan became part of the Soviet Union, the authorities took all the buildings and wealth of the aristocracy and handed them over to ordinary people. The museum was no exception. Let's go home,' she said. 'Nana is cooking up a feast to celebrate.'

The family was already at the table: Uncle Telman, cheerful but not convinced that Mama's ambition was appropriate, and my seventeen-year old Uncle Salman, indifferent, or perhaps unimpressed, as he did not utter a word. The moment Mama and I were seated, Nana brought through a large pan of *piti*. Her way of praising

Mama's achievement was to complain: if only she knew and appreciated how many dresses Nana had made to save up the money to afford this job.

Listening to Nana's grumble about the financial strain Mama's job caused her, I wondered whether it was meant to reward Mama for ending her 'illegal relationship' and to distract her from attempting to do anything stupid again. No one ever mentioned the 'incident' with Mama's wrists. I did my best to forget it too, despite the flashbacks. They did not cause me pain, just numbness, which turned into restlessness and panic when I saw blood on the TV or did not know Mama's whereabouts. I pushed the thoughts away and examined the plump beef tomatoes in the middle of the table.

Baba's booming voice brought me back into the room and I realised that I was still staring at the tomatoes. Baba's face was shining with pride, as he quizzed Mama on the details of her job. He seemed to be the only one who genuinely celebrated Mama. After a few minutes, the aroma of stewed lamb with fluffy potatoes and chickpeas on my plate distracted me from their exchange.

★★★

It did not take me long to fall in love with Mama's new job. She picked me up from school most days, as the museum was nearby. Her accountant Nazila was particularly friendly and forced some candies on me from time to time. While at the museum, I was allowed to play in the spacious halls, look round the various exhibits or do my homework at the other end of Mama's enormous dark wood desk.

'A typical show-off of a man,' Mama said, 'to choose a desk too big for the room. And he left it piled with work he hadn't done!'

She had to work so hard. The museum records were a mess. Some exhibits had even gone missing.

'This is why no one wanted this job,' she murmured, trying to match the records with all the ancient jewellery, rugs and coins scattered around her. 'What am I going to do if there's an inspection?'

Because Mama worried so much about the missing objects, Baba used all his connections to get in touch with people who owned objects like those that had disappeared. Many helped out: a cousin sold them an ancient oriental silk rug, which shimmered like a peacock's tail, and an aunt gave her great-grandmother's golden jewellery set, for a fair price, of course. Not all the objects could be replaced. Sometimes I would hear Mama talking about them in her sleep.

★★★

The solution to Mama's troubles came as a throwaway remark one Saturday afternoon. We were all sitting around the dining room table.

'Four *pyatyorkas* in one day!' Baba beamed at me, showing his fake teeth. His face was covered in grey stubble as it always was after his nightshifts at the local taxi dispatching company. 'Not just top marks, but with a plus. She is the brainy one in this family!'

'She is always the best, my granddaughter.' Nana adjusted her glasses as she returned to sewing the dress she was working on for one of her customers. There were not many nice clothes in the shops and Nana's skills were always in demand. 'You are the light of my eyes!' she said softly, so only I could hear.

Ignoring everyone else, Mama stared at some paperwork she had brought home from work. Uncle Telman sipped on his black tea and tried to engage Mama in conversation from time to time but she shrugged her shoulders in response. If she spoke at all, she could only squeeze out a word or two at a time.

'Oh, stop fretting about it, Maryam. If you are so worried about those missing items, let's stage a break in. I'll go and do it, and if something goes wrong, they can blame me. I can't bear to see you withering like this over some half-broken stuff no one even cares about.'

'You would do that for me?' Mama said quietly. As she raised her head to look at him, we could all see her lips trembling, tears welling up in her eyes.

'This is what family is for. We may fight, we may even cause great hurt, but in times of need we will be there for each other. That is how a family loves, is it not?' said Uncle Telman.

'We love fiercely in our family,' said Baba. 'Who amongst us would not be willing to die for the others, eh?'

Mama mouthed a 'thank you' and the others celebrated the moment with black tea in pear-shaped glasses.

'I'll bring the museum floorplans tomorrow,' Mama said to Uncle Telman, before setting her paperwork aside.

★★★

The next evening, as the adults gathered in the living room to discuss the staged break-in, I was shushed off to bed. I crept into the darkened hallway as soon as the kitchen comings and goings had finished and positioned myself by a crack in the living room door. There they all were, Baba in his smart suit ready for the night shift, Uncle Salman in his tracksuit still sweaty after his evening workout at the local gym, Mama distant and thoughtful, and Nana like a bull ready to charge, poring over some large sheets of paper on the now cleared table.

'These plans were drawn up by an amateur,' exclaimed Uncle Telman. 'I would have failed my degree if my drafting was this bad.'

'But are they enough?' Baba asked.

'Sure. I can see all the museum's exits and entrances. There is a network of rooms and passages under the ground floor, which may prove useful.'

'And there's the refuse shoots and air-con,' added Uncle Salman.

'Too small to be considered for me. No, Salman, I repeat, you are not coming!' Uncle Telman snapped back.

She gave him the key to the museum; the entry was easy, as there were no residential houses around the building, with a deserted backyard. The museum was not deemed to be worth paying for a night watchman, and the likelihood of police patrolling the streets at that time was low. Uncle Telman could climb the stairs to the top floor of the museum, break a window to suggest a break-in, and then enter three exhibition rooms to mess up some artefacts with his gloved hands. Mama took pains to remind him not to take anything out, just create an appearance that someone had entered and stolen some items. Mama would report the break-in to the police the next morning, then sign off the objects that had been missing all along.

I held my breath as Uncle Telman swathed himself in his darkest coat, to blend into the night and placed the heaviest hammer in the house into a pocket.

It looked like a scene from a movie like *Bluff*, a comedy Mama and I had watched that week in the central cinema. Then I thought, what if their bluff did not work? Baba had got eleven years in prison after an explosion on his oil rig killed several people. What if Mama and Uncle got caught? What would my life be without them? As they started to put things away, I scurried back to my bed where I cried myself silently to sleep.

I woke up suddenly, groggy and disorientated, and reached for Mama but her bed was empty and cold. I tiptoed to the hall and saw the yellow of electric lights spilling out from the living room. Through the crack in the door, I watched Mama fiddling with her golden watch where the scars were on her wrist, as she always did when she was nervous. Nana was slamming and pacing in the kitchen like a caged tiger and Uncle Salman was sulking on his favourite armchair. I couldn't see Baba; perhaps he had gone on his night shift. I crept back to my bed and resolved to stay awake until Uncle Telman returned.

I did not think anyone slept easily that night. Mama kept sighing in her bed across from mine, after climbing in fully clothed under her blanket. I heard Nana's uneven tread to and from the kitchen, taps turning on and off, the creak of the back door as she slipped out to smoke.

I wanted to stay awake, so I did not miss anything of

the drama. I managed for an hour or so. The last thing I remembered hearing was the tick-tock of Baba's tall case clock in the hall.

The next time I opened my eyes, Mama was shaking me by my shoulder.

'It's time for school.'

'What's happened to Uncle Telman? Is he back?'

'No time to talk. I'll be late for work. Hurry.'

Mama's face looked firm, so I dressed quickly, butterflies dancing in my head as well as my stomach. Mama got us both buttered bread from the kitchen, which we ate, after we'd pelted to the bus stop. On the bus, Mama insisted we chatted about what I would be doing at school and blanked all my whispered questions. As she leant to kiss me goodbye, she said: 'Remember, we don't talk about family things with anyone!'

★★★

That day, I could hardly wait for Mama to pick me up from school. I was not even interested in receiving *pyatorkas* in maths class. It felt so trivial compared to what was at stake for our family.

When Mama greeted me at the waist-height stone water fountains by the school entrance later, she seemed as relaxed and happy as on the day she'd first told me about her job at the museum, but she still would not tell me anything until we arrived home where the whole family were gathered in the living room.

Nana was busy making *kuftas*, meatballs with potatoes and chickpeas, sprinkled with dried basil and mint. She served Baba first, then my uncles. I nestled next to Mama at the table and spooned myself a big helping of juicy homemade gherkins, usually my favourites, but I was so impatient to hear Mama's news I had lost my appetite temporarily.

Once everyone settled, all eyes were on Mama, but she would never rush a good story. We waited as she cleared her throat and sipped some compote drink Nana preserved in three-litre jars, then told us about her day.

'I arrived at work to find Nazila frantically cleaning every surface she could think of with a cloth and mop. She's my accountant and up until today I thought she was rather dim, to be honest, though very kind, indeed. Somehow, she figured out that the break-in was staged. I guess nothing was missing from the artefacts, so it made sense that she tried to eliminate all fingerprints. When I walked into my office, she was on all fours with her bulging backside cleaning the floor with a cloth.'

As the tension subsided in my shoulders, my appetite returned, and I stabbed the meatball with my fork.

'It was so funny! I had to pretend to be shocked by the news,' Mama continued, pulling a surprised face.

'Very convincing, I'm sure,' chuckled Uncle Telman. 'And what of the evil burglar?' He contorted his features and snarled sharply, making me jump.

Our living room echoed with laughter. Nana and I clung together and laughed uncontrollably. Mama had to shush us to finish her tale: 'Then we had to call the Police.'

Silence stilled us all.

'What did they do?' Uncle Telman was the first to ask.

'They said they would send someone straight away.

Their best man, Lieutenant Aliyev. We rushed about making sure everything looked right, and then…'

'Yes,' said Baba impatiently.

'He didn't turn up until after lunch,' Mama grinned. 'And he was very, very fat with the biggest moustache I had ever seen. And lots of extra badges on his jacket. Proud as a peacock.'

'I know that name,' Baba cut in. 'How old was he?'

'Close to retirement I think.'

'Hmph. I think I know him. Nasty temper and so bossy.'

'Well, he hasn't changed a bit. He had a skinny little assistant with him. He insisted on talking to everyone, even though it had happened at night. He poked around all the rooms.'

'Even though it was clear where the 'burglar' entered?' Uncle Telman snorted.

'Yes. He was particularly interested in the broken glass.' Mama said.

'Because it had the wrong scatter pattern,' said Uncle Salman, barely looking up from the TV guide he was perusing. 'I told you if you broke it from the inside that they'd notice. But would you listen?' He shrugged.

'Is that true, Maryam? Did he notice?' Baba said, leaning forwards.

'Perhaps,' she said, as we all gasped. 'He spent a long time looking at it, and then…'

She paused. We paused.

'He told us it was obviously a professional job, that we should sign off all the missing objects from the museum's roster, had another cup of tea and biscuits, and left. I think he was hoping for a bribe but lost hope halfway through talking to the museum staff. It's not the best-paid job in the city.'

While Baba and Nana spoke to each other in half whispers, Mama turned towards her brothers and chuckled.

'Your faces. Stop worrying! It's all over.'

3.

PIONEER

Kirovabad, Azerbaijan S.S.R., 1983

Crisis averted, Mama directed all her energies into advancing her career. One sure way to progress was to become a member of the Communist Party. To do that, Mama had to show leadership and enthusiasm as a member of the Komsomol – the All-Union Leninist Young Communist League.

Whilst Nana and Baba recognised that becoming a member of the Communist Party was the only way up the career ladder, they did not necessarily want their daughter to climb it. Nana believed that Mama's primary duty was to help her in the home, then, when the time and person was right, remarry and become a respectable wife and mistress of her own.

Mama, however, did what she always did. She started organising events for young leaders, keeping it a secret from the rest of the family: I had to guard the bedroom door from Nana's unexpected invasion, while she had hushed conversations with her comrades about the forthcoming events.

One day, she collected me from school and instructed

26

me to play at the museum until she returned. She looked beautiful, in a snow-white long-sleeve shirt and black skirt with two large red embroidered roses shimmering around her ankles.

'Why can't I come along?'

She waved me off with her hand, not giving an explanation, and clattered down the stone steps of the museum. I returned to Mama's office and watched her climb into an overcrowded car. Face pressed on the cold windowpane, I recognised her Russian friends from the Komsomol.

Feeling lost and lonely, I wandered around her office and tried to find things to do, besides my homework. When her plump friendly accountant Nazila checked on me later, I felt so grumpy that I ignored her smile, furrowed my eyebrows in pretend concentration on my homework, and did not respond to her offer of tea and candy, even though I was hungry.

I felt anxious at Mama's absence. What if she did not come back before the museum closed for the day? What if Nana was angry with both of us for being so late back? The huge gilt museum clock was striking seven and my face was wet with tears when she finally returned. She looked tired and tense.

'Hurry up,' was all she said before grabbing my hand and leading me outside to the same car. I was squashed in the back seat between Mama and men I did not know. They smelt of tobacco and old books. Neither of us spoke, though Mama squeezed me with a sweaty hand. I think she was worrying about Nana too and my tears continued to roll silently down my face.

The car stopped at the top of the street to avoid anyone seeing us travelling with strangers. Young women were not meant to have male friends. They would usually only travel in a car with their immediate male relatives, or a husband, because gossip was often dangerous, sometimes deadly. I dried my face on my sleeve ready for Nana's wrath. Mama was breaking the rules again! I feared for her as well as myself because she had made me part of this. Nana seemed to have a sixth sense when it came to me lying. I sighed and stretched my lips into a fake smile. Despite my rumbling tummy and quivering heart, I had to put on my best performance ever. I stepped out of the car primed to lie, again.

★★★

A few days later, as the school's out bell rang, I easily spotted Mama in the crowd of parents near the fountains. She was always the best dressed and her heels put her above most others.

'Look what I have, Mama,' I shouted. I ran up to her, waving two letters in my outstretched hand.

'They want to transfer me to the special English class. I'm in the top thirty of 180 pupils,' I beamed proudly. I had been told it was a great achievement. As Mama read on, I added, 'We get to do English from Year Two, everyone else has to wait for Year Four. In the special class, you study English every single day, unlike the others who have only two classes a week. Isn't it wonderful?'

'Why do you even need English?' Mama shrugged and stuffed the letter in her bag.

'But Mama, all the best pupils will be in that class.'

'Is Tarana transferring too?' she asked, without looking at me. She was already opening the other letter.

Tarana was the other star student in my class. I was in constant competition with her. So far, our results were almost identical.

'No, I don't think so.'

'I wonder why? Her mother is well connected. If it were a good idea, Tarana would be the first to go. Anyway, Lidiya Ivanovna is such a good teacher. You should stay where you are.'

I did not like Lidiya Ivanovna. She looked like *Koschei* the Immortal, a scary character from a Russian fairy tale. Old and bony, with a jutting chin, she would hit children's hands with a ruler if they did not write neatly or gave her the wrong answer. Reading and writing were easy for me because I learnt before I started school, so she was reasonably kind to me, but I was still scared of her.

Mama brushed off my disappointment as she read the second letter. It was about my becoming a Young Pioneer, a member of The All-Union Pioneer Organisation, dedicated to Lenin. Only three girls had been selected from my class, as a reward for excellent marks. We would be attending the inaugural enrolment ceremony. The average pupils would have to wait until several weeks later, whilst those with the lowest marks and bad behaviour would be kept back for a whole year. Membership was supposed to be optional, but few refused it.

'This news, however, is excellent.' Mama bent down to clasp me tightly and delivered a kiss to both my cheeks. 'I think today is a chewing gum day,' she added, as she walked away. I hesitated, biting my lip. I had so wanted to be in that English class.

'Come on, Gulush! Before I change my mind!' Mama turned as she reached the first corner. There was no point in arguing, I knew, as I ran after her.

The rest of the family reacted the same way. Nana said she did not expect anything less of me. Of course, I had to be the first to become a pioneer in my class.

'As for English,' said Uncle Telman, 'who needs it in the Soviet Union? You will never have the need to travel abroad!'

They all laughed at such an idea. They had no clue that I disagreed with them.

Ever since I had seen Princess Diana, I had wanted to go to England. My heart swelled up each time I spotted her on TV. I did not know why. It was such an impossible dream for a young girl like me, but I kept it burning bright just the same. I would learn English, work at an embassy here and then one day I would be allowed to go abroad. I had heard some of the older pioneers talk of such things. Once you were trusted, you could go anywhere. I was determined that would be me. I wanted to be remembered, like the princess, one day. It might have felt wrong to think like that, but why else was I born, I thought. I had learnt from her example, and my teachers, that there could be more to life than making a good marriage and birthing children.

I did not dare to share this with anyone because I was afraid of being mocked and teased, so when Mama told me I would stay in Lidiya Ivanovna's class I did not argue and hid my upset until I was alone in the dark of our bedroom.

★★★

My Young Pioneer initiation ceremony was in late Spring, in the Officers' Park, where an eternal flame memorial commemorated the heroes of World War II. It was not my first time there. On several occasions I had performed for war veterans on my violin in the park, with the rest of my music school, as part of celebrations of the end of World War II. I remembered standing tall in a white shirt with a black bell skirt and playing my violin in the front row amongst the best twenty pupils of my music school.

Now waiting for the ceremony to start, to take the oath to be a good pioneer, my teeth chattered in the cold wind. My school uniform of a white long-sleeve shirt and navy skirt that modestly covered my knees felt insubstantial in the chilly morning.

To prepare for the ceremony, I had had to memorise *The Young Pioneer Leader's Handbook*. Some things in it made sense: to always work hard on my studies and to follow Lenin's path, but other things were more challenging. I was supposed to set up an atheist's corner at home, with anti-religious pictures and poems. I fretted about it for weeks. I did not want to offend Nana or Great Uncle Hussein, her brother, who was a Mullah. When I finally told Mama my worries, she reassured me that no one would really come to check our house for my corner and of course I could still join the pioneers if I did not have one.

'Guliyeva Gulara,' my school director called my name, the surname first, of course.

I walked slowly towards the war memorial, as if I were moving underwater. I was aware of dressed-up schoolteachers, some parents in suits and about fifteen other eight-year-old children waiting for their turn, standing in a semi-circle around the eternal flame. Older pioneers stood solemnly in the back, ready to support the new generation. My knees were wobbling as I spoke my pledge.

'I, Guliyeva Gulara, joining the ranks of the Vladimir Ilyich Lenin All-Union Pioneer Organisation, in the presence of my comrades, solemnly promise to passionately love and cherish my Motherland; to live as the great Lenin bade us to; as the Communist Party teaches us to; as required by the laws of the Pioneers of the Soviet Union.'

Annoyed that my voice crackled in places, I fidgeted until an older girl from my school approached me and tied a scarlet scarf around my neck. It gave me a strange sense of elation, as if I had grown up a little. I returned to where I stood before, my face flushed, feeling hot and cold at the same time.

Once everyone gave their pledge, the school director jutted his chin up, making his lower lip protrude more than usual, and gave a solemn speech. After a round of applause, the deputy director smoothed down her stern jacket and black ankle-length skirt, stepped forward and stood in front us like a statue until everyone's eyes were resting on her stout figure.

'Pioneers, to fight for the cause of the Communist Party of the Soviet Union, be prepared!' She issued the oath I was to hear from now on.

'Always prepared!' we answered in unison and saluted with our right arms, bent at the elbow with the palm hovering near our foreheads.

For the next few weeks, I enjoyed being a pioneer: it made me feel superior in the class, though I tried not to show it. However, the scarlet scarves singled us out. From some of our classmates there was respect, from others, jealousy. It was sometimes difficult to be a pioneer.

★★★

Unlike my early initiation as a Young Pioneer, Mama's membership of the Communist Party was not forthcoming. This was due in part to an unexpected turn of events one Sunday afternoon.

It was unusually peaceful at home. Baba was in a good mood, relaxing on the sofa in the living room listening to me play the violin. The smell of *ajabsandal* – a colourful mix of aubergines, beef tomatoes, green peppers and fluffy potatoes – wafted from the kitchen where Nana hummed as she washed the pots. The vacuum purred and clunked next door as Mama cleaned. It was difficult to concentrate on my piece.

'Gulush,' said Baba, 'when are you going to learn a simple Azerbaijani folk song?'

'But Baba, they don't teach us those at music school. I have to play Bach and Beethoven to pass my exams.'

'Well, it's not to my taste. Put your violin down and let's watch television for a while.'

After a good night's sleep, Baba seemed softer and kinder, so I quickly snuggled up to him, feeling happy and loved as the TV warmed up and the grainy picture emerged.

I saw her first because Baba was checking the programme times in the paper. I froze in shock as Baba said: 'Coverage of the… no, we shan't watch that, turn it to…' I felt him tense up. On the small black and white screen, there was Mama!

'What?' Baba gasped.

She was on a stage, holding a microphone, speaking for the Communist Party. I instantly recognised the outfit; it was the one she had worn that night she'd left me at the museum.

It was too late to distract Baba. I could not move as I waited for the disaster to unfold. Mama's lies had found her out, as I feared they would. Who would beat her this time?

The vacuum was silent now. She must have started dusting. Baba's voice sounded unnervingly calm: 'Oh Maryam! Maryam, come look at this,' his voice sang out.

'Coming, I've nearly finished.' Mama appeared, yellow cloth in hand. She dropped it when she saw the screen.

Baba's stubbly face stretched into a thin smile: 'Doesn't she look exactly like you?' He waved towards the screen. I saw Mama's whole body tighten up as she stared from behind him at the TV. Had she known they were filming? Her face seemed to say not. She bit her lip, blinking, as if wishing the rug she stood on would swallow her up.

'You've got a twin!' He laughed. 'But she doesn't have your style. Those roses are too much.'

Why couldn't he see it really was Mama? The picture may have been in black and white, the sound down low, but I thought it was obvious.

'Even a pretty face like yours can't stop this being boring. I wonder if her family knows what she's up to?' Baba mused.

'Yes.' After so long a pause, the answer Mama squeezed through her pale lips seemed out of place.

I looked into her glassy eyes, silently asking, 'What should I do?'

Her reanimation answered me. Like a video taken off pause, she rushed into the kitchen. I understood instantly. Baba had not recognised her, but Nana would. I shook, imagining what might follow, as I tried, without success, to get Baba to change channels or listen to my favourite fairy tale on the vinyl player nestled in the corner.

I sat miserably at his feet, colouring in a map for homework, ready to spring up in front of the screen if Mama's attempts to keep Nana in the kitchen failed. The programme seemed so long. I could hear Mama joining Nana in all her favourite stories as the pots clattered and pans sizzled. My shoulders twitched at every sound. If Nana saw her that would be the end of Mama's career. A marriage and a home to mind would follow, or much worse. I had heard the stories about what happened to other women.

The worst moment came when Baba asked me to turn the TV's volume up: 'Your Nana's voice could cut through steel.' He laughed at his own joke.

I did not. I took my time, then fiddled, with sweaty hands, pretending I had forgotten which knob was which, until he snapped: 'Do you want me to come and do it for you?'

Luckily, as the volume rose, the picture changed. I gasped a prayer of gratitude and slumped back on the floor.

'Perhaps she'll be back again, that twin of your mother's. Read her name out to me if they show it. I can't see from here. Such tiny writing, they use.'

He returned to his paper, and I waited. Suppose the announcer read out the names? Mama's face was flashed up at the end of the programme, as the martial-style music played, but Baba missed it and the clear lettering under it.

I felt shaky as I got up. 'Going to get a glass of water,' I said. I slipped into the kitchen, tugged on Mama's apron and relayed the end of the ordeal with a very small smile.

Tension deflated from her face as she smiled, but I could still feel her trembling.

'That was close,' Mama said as soon as our bedroom door was shut that night. 'Leave some room for me,' she said, sitting down on her bed.

'I was so frightened...' I started to say.

'Hush, hush. I know. Listen, I won't be getting involved in any more events like that, I promise. I'm going to concentrate on my job. If I do well, Nana and Baba will be happy. And you, of course,' she added, catching my expression in the lamplight. 'The Communist Party will have to wait,' she said, opening my reading book, 'for now.'

I pursed my lips and frowned at that.

'Joking, joking!' Mama raised her hands in submission. 'Now, where were we. Read from here.'

As I started, I could not help wondering if she really meant it.

4.

A CHANGE OF DESTINATION

Kirovabad, Azerbaijan S.S.R., 1983

I stood on tiptoes and craned my neck, trying to see beyond the crowd of jostling parents and children, to the fountains. She definitely was not there. Neither was Baba or anyone else who usually came to collect me. I only had five *gapiks* in my pocket. Not enough for the two buses home, a journey I had never done alone before. I pulled my lip in trying not to cry and was just about to go and look for the janitor when I heard someone call me: 'Gulya! Over here. Gulya,' a woman's voice repeated. I turned to see Sara *Khala*, Tarana's mother, looking at me.

I ran towards her.

'You're coming back to our flat now,' she said, as Tarana beamed. 'Your mother is picking you up later. She did tell you. You forgot, I suppose. Typical child. Hurry now, I have enough to do already.'

I knew Mama had not told me, but I also knew not to protest. A chill settled in my stomach. What had happened this time? What was Mama doing?

What worried me most was the invitation to Sara *Khala*'s flat. I was never allowed to go to other people's homes, unless Nana had given her express permission, and she had not said anything either that morning. Images of Mama's ill time flashed through my head, alongside a host of imaginary fears.

'What a frowny face,' Sara *Khala* said, more gently. 'Gulya, everything is fine. Your mother will be coming soon. In the meantime, you can do your school homework with Tarana and listen to my new music if you like. I have Zeynab Khanlarova's new vinyl.'

Zeynab Khanlarova's traditional Azerbaijani music was not to my liking because she looked like Mama's spinster cousin in heavy make-up. I preferred Alla Pugacheva's songs on Russian television but kept my opinion to myself.

Tarana smiled and took my slightly sweaty hand in her warm one.

'We will have a good time,' she promised.

She was my best friend; or had been until recently. I could still taste the bitter disappointment that had settled on me after the recent class *starosta* election episode.

Our teacher, the aforementioned Lidiya Ivanova, had asked us all who we might like to stand in an election for class *starosta* – head girl or head boy of the class. My hand shot up to nominate Tarana, several people echoed my recommendation, but many more suggested me.

'Gulya, Gulya,' they cried out. I was surprised to find so many of them liked me that much. When my election as a *starosta* was later announced, I felt like my insides were jumping up and down with pride. As I carried the class register from our maths lesson to the arts class, I felt taller.

The family were proud too, but the celebration cake Nana baked me soon had to be renamed, because the next day our teacher announced: 'Children, our friend Tarana was terribly upset by what happened yesterday. She feels—' Lidiya Ivanovna seemed to struggle to find the right words— 'I feel, that after consideration of everything, Tarana should be the *starosta* for this class. Gulya already has so many commitments.'

Lidiya Ivanovna avoided my eyes during this speech. I felt a fire fuming up inside me, but she snapped: 'That will be all. Back to your studies now.' And that told me I was not expected to protest.

Still unbelieving, I tried to concentrate on Russian grammar, but my mind kept wandering, for I knew something the others obviously did not.

Whilst standing waiting for the class register that morning, outside the secretarial office, I had seen Tarana's mother carrying a large carrier bag into the school. The same bag was sitting under Lidiya Ivanovna's desk for the rest of that day. The image of our teacher bearing her 'prize' to the nearest bus stop at the end of lessons still swam in my head as we trudged through unfamiliar streets to Tarana's home in a five-storey block of flats. How long would I have to be there?

My misery grew as she broke the silence by asking, in her soft voice: 'What do you do in the evenings?'

It seemed a very silly question. Although we had not really spoken much since the election, I had been volunteering to be in other groups, away from her, whenever I got the chance. She already knew a lot about me, I thought. For some reason, I replied: 'Oh, nothing much. Sometimes we play a treasure-hunt game, in our garden.' I stressed the last three words. 'Mama digs small holes and hides all sorts of lovely things, like sweets and special stones for me to run about and find with all my neighbourhood friends. The first seeker who finds one wins an extra prize!'

I watched Tarana's face fall. Her plump, whitish lips trembled and momentarily she looked so sad and lonely that I regretted telling such a tale. I knew those feelings myself and I wished I could have played the game I had just described for real.

In truth it was someone else's experience I had borrowed. Uncle Telman's secret girlfriend Sevil had told me about her family playing it when they were 'babysitting' me one night. I wished I had the magical childhood that Sevil had seemed to have, with lots of brothers and a huge house in Berlin, when her father was serving in the Soviet army there.

Tarana and I kept our silence until we all started to climb the grey concrete stairs of her block. Tarana was good with books, but not with people. She started jabbering on about all our classmates that lived nearby. She still did not understand how upset I had been about her being *starosta* instead of me, even though I had explained it to her as calmly as I could the next day. I just nodded in the right places as if I were listening.

Dim light poured through large windows on the staircase. Thick dust caked the windows, which were broken in several places. Walking behind her, I admired Tarana's two thick brown braids, dangling to her waistline. I ran my hand through my own short chestnut hair. Mama did not have the patience to style it like Nana did for her when she was little. Every couple of months, ignoring my pleas, Mama would chop it all off, making me look like a boy.

Stepping through the door of Tarana's flat, for the first time ever, I felt like I had been transported to a different world. I took my shoes off and my feet sank into the warmth of a cosy deep pile carpet. There were carpets everywhere. Thick and colourful with beautiful hand-woven patterns, they covered the floors and the walls of the living room. They looked expensive. I knew about carpets because when my family was short of money, they would debate which carpet to sell first.

I flopped into a large, cream sofa next to Tarana and stared in awe at the hefty crystal chandelier. Above me, the German, Madonna porcelain tea set trimmed with gold and its neighbouring treasures were displayed in fine, wooden, glass-fronted cabinets. I was just imagining how long it all took to clean when a young girl entered carefully carrying a tray of refreshments. She was dressed in a simple brown dress, like a country girl, her hair in long plaits. As soon as she had put the tray down, she scurried back into the kitchen without a word. I stared curiously after her.

'She's a distant cousin, from my home village,' Sara *Khala* said. She seemed anxious to explain the girl's presence to me. 'She is staying with us whilst she studies and helps from time to time with the chores. Tarana is hopeless with them. I expect you help your mama much better.' She smiled.

I had heard Mama talk about 'pretend Communists', people who spoke about equality and the collective, but who lived like kings and tyrants at home. Sara *Khala* was obviously one of them, using her cousin as a servant, like the wicked stepmother did to Cinderella in the story.

What would Mama say when she saw it all, I wondered, but was soon distracted by the treats in front of me. There were little buttered sandwiches of cheese and salami, slices of chocolate cream cake, succulent apples, plump walnuts and imported, foil-wrapped Russian chocolates.

'Help yourself. It's just a little something we have before dinner. Tarana works so hard,' Sara *Khala* said.

I hesitated. Nana did not like me to eat between meals. Sara *Khala* filled a plate and thrust it on me. I started to slowly chew a piece of salami since I could not think of anything to say. Tarana was already busy eating.

'You enjoy school?' Sara *Khala* said through a mouthful of food. She had huge white teeth. 'What subjects do you like?'

'I love them all,' I replied, blushing with the effort of lying to please.

Traitor, I called myself, as I extolled the virtues of our school, whilst images of the reality crowded my head. As a star pupil I had never been punished by my teacher, but I had seen Lidiya Ivanovna whack children's hands raw with a ruler. I had choked back the claustrophobia during the regular gas-mask drill, in case the Soviet Union was attacked, and had borne the humiliation of marching up and down the playground chanting:

'One, two, three, four,

Here comes the glorious, pioneer squad'.

Worst of all to me, as a child, was having to memorise long extracts of patriotic poetry and reciting it to large audiences of parents and invited dignitaries. I was determined Tarana's mother would not know my true feelings.

She continued to munch her food, oblivious to my unease.

'Tarana says she loves them all, too. I guess your subjects are not that difficult yet. The first three years are just to build up a foundation. Come next year, I bet you won't have the time to share a delightful tea with a friend.' She laughed. 'I doubt you'll have any free time at all. I fondly remember my schooldays.'

She glanced at Tarana and pointed at her school uniform. Tarana stood up immediately and went to her bedroom to change.

Sara *Khala* leant in towards me, as soon as Tarana was out of earshot, and whispered: 'Is Tarana doing well at school?'

'Yes, she's brilliant at everything,' I said vehemently.

Sara *Khala* beamed. 'Of course, she would be as clever as I was. And her father.' She dreamily pushed her coloured curls back from her intense brown eyes.

I managed not to giggle at her mention of Tarana's father. Sara *Khala* was the only single parent I had ever met, never married. I had heard Mama and some of the other mothers share their views on that as we walked to the bus together.

Sara *Khala* had apparently chosen a man in her department, pursued him and got pregnant, deliberately. She had spent her pregnancy in Baku, returning with a baby girl in her arms and no remorse. Tarana's father was married with four daughters of his own. 'His poor wife is so patient with him,' the gossips had tutted. I sometimes wondered what they said about my mama when she was not with them.

Having withstood Sara *Khala*'s barrage of questions, we sat in awkward silence until Tarana reappeared and invited me to see her bedroom.

Two of the walls in her bedroom were covered with carpets, as well, but the wall that captured my attention was the one with bookshelves reaching from floor to ceiling, full of all sorts of books. Being a precocious reader (I had a reading age well above my actual age, even before I started school), I quickly recognised classics like Tolstoy and Chekov that I had not yet read, alongside those I had, like Pushkin, Mayakovsky and Lermontov. I pulled Mayakovsky's poetry book and immediately opened the page on my favourite poem 'What is Good and What is Bad?' I replaced it on the shelf and continued my exploration, while Tarana fiddled with her school bag.

Most of the books we had at home were for adults, some difficult to understand, but Tarana's collection seemed to contain everything I wanted to read, including illustrated books, which looked far more colourful and fun than the dusty volumes at home. I opened the pages of Pushkin's *The Tale of Tsar Saltan* and gasped at the delightful, glossy painting of 'The Swan Princess' and the rich tapestry of the robes in the illustration of 'The Merchant's Visit to Tsar Saltan'.

'Tarana, could I borrow a book?'

'I expect so. But I'll have to ask Mum first, before I lend my things out.'

She sprinted to the living room, closing the door behind her.

Overwhelmed by the possible choices, I decided to inspect Tarana's room until she returned. There was a beautiful dressing table, with a large mirror and vibrant, expensive-looking bottles of perfume. One drawer was open, filled with lipsticks, mascaras, hairbrushes, combs and peeping from underneath them, some money. I stared at the five and ten ruble notes, more money than I had ever had in all the eight years of my life. I felt a flutter of excitement, then wished Tarana would return straight away, as temptation started to tug at me. With so many notes, she would not miss just a few. As if in a trance, I saw my hand shoot out, grab a five ruble note and stuff it into my skirt pocket. I told myself off and was about to put it back when Tarana burst through the door.

'Mum says you can borrow anything you like, as long as you promise to take good care of it.' She was so excited to please me that she did not notice how I jumped when she entered. 'Sorry I took so long. The girl is cooking dinner and I went to see what it was.'

'I haven't chosen one yet,' I confessed, moving away from the dressing table closer to the shelves, 'you have so many.'

'I know. Some of them are family…'

A rap at the door cut her off. Mama's head poked round the door. I whooped in relief and rushed to hug her. She was all right, but in a hurry as usual, so after brief thank-yous and goodbyes, we were soon out on the street.

Only then did I notice her face. The traces of black mascara she wiped off her face told me she had been crying. Above us the tree skeletons were waving their bare arms in the chilling dusk.

'What's happened?' I asked, as Mama set a fast pace down the pavement. A cold breeze peeled the collar of my coat from my neck. 'What's happened?' I repeated and pulled the sleeve of her fake fur coat.

My question hung in the air for several paces, then she stopped and faced me. I could see her pressing the corners of her mouth tight together to stop herself crying.

'They are taking Salman to Afghanistan!' she announced, then hugged me close.

'Who are they? Why to Afghanistan?' I demanded.

'The Army, the Soviet army, the so-called Red Army. We are going to the Komissariat now.'

She looked at my puzzled face and explained more.

'The Komissariat handles military conscription. All eighteen-year-old boys get conscripted. It's just… Afghanistan is a dangerous place. There's a war.' She choked on her words, then started walking again. 'Baba is trying to change Salman's destination.'

'How?'

'With zaems.'

Zaems worked like money. On the first day of every month, Nana and Baba tried to buy a new one for fifty rubles. They also bought a newspaper and sat with a stack of their zaems, to check the dense lists of numbers on the double spread of a newspaper to see whether they had won anything.

I tried to ask more questions about Uncle Salman, but they only made Mama cry. I fell silent, listening to the sound of Mama's high heels puncturing the air. Streetlights twinkled in the distance on the main street, Lenin Avenue. Uniform five-storeyed apartment blocks towered above us like giant matchstick boxes.

When we reached the Komissariat, I saw Nana, family

and friends outside in the pool of light cast by the lamp over its imposing wooden entrance door.

They were gathered round Uncle Salman, who stood impassively with a large sports bag between his legs. Tears sprang into my eyes as I imagined him being taken so far away. Would he ever come back?

As we waited, I remembered how he used to tease me when I was little, singing my favourite song all wrong. It went:

I am a little girl,
I don't go to school.
I haven't seen Lenin,
But it'd be the dream come true.

He would change the last line to 'I hope I never do'! and sing his version whenever he picked me up from kindergarten. Even then I feared the trouble he might get into for saying such things. Now, as he stood awaiting his fate, I was willing to forgive him for everything. I pressed myself against him and he ruffled my hair. Seeing everyone's anxious faces, I felt suddenly small and helpless.

A battered, white Jiguli car drew up next to us and another family spilled out of it. The woman was crying loudly. The driver barked at her to calm down, then left her with a tall, bony teenage boy, by the car. His companion, a man who looked similar to him, offered a cigarette.

'They've only reported six deaths in Afghanistan so far, but I heard there were thousands. Our boys are used like cannon fodder by the Russians.' He spat emphatically on the ground, stomped on his cigarette butt and immediately lit another one. For a few seconds, the burning matchstick illuminated the deep wrinkles in his dark, angry face.

'I can't believe they take them all on the same day,' the other man said. His voice shook with emotion.

'They know families may hide their sons. Whoever's got the money and connections can sort things out on the day. Needless to say, they shear you like a sheep.'

As I listened to their conversation, I felt my stomach tie into a knot. I understood why everyone was so worried now. Uncle Salman could be hurt, or even killed, for real. Others must have heard them talking, because the anxious murmur of neighbours and relatives started to grow stronger, until the door of the Komissariat opened and Baba and Uncle Telman appeared.

The crowd by the doors of the Komissariat parted as they moved warrior-like towards Uncle Salman. Their faces betrayed nothing. I saw Nana peering up at Baba, her breath in short, quiet sobs.

'It's time,' Baba said, embracing Uncle Salman.

Nana pursed her wrinkled mouth to suppress any sounds and drew closer, to listen.

'I gave them all I had,' said Baba to my uncle. 'You are going to Feodosia in Crimea. Don't try to be a hero. Don't stick out. You'll work in the kitchen and there will be plenty of food. I'll come and visit.'

Everyone who could reach kissed, hugged or patted Uncle Salman, who smiled gratefully at Baba, until two soldiers came to tear him from us.

The door banged shut behind them and, cloaked in darkness, we headed home in tears.

★★★

In the sad, empty days that followed Uncle Salman's departure, it was Tarana's five ruble note, hidden in the piano, that burnt a hole in my heart. I could not buy myself anything with it for fear of the questions Nana might ask. For days, I tried not to think about it and tensed up every time Tarana spoke to me in class. Although she seemed unaware of my sin, our friendship, already fragile, dwindled away, as those rubles built an invisible wall between us.

As Nana's birthday approached, I suddenly had an idea how to cheer her up and get rid of the money at the same time.

One afternoon, as Mama was making my favourite marble cake, I broached the subject with her.

'Mama, let's buy Nana a present for her birthday. She was saying she doesn't have anything to wear under her favourite dress. It's too transparent. Maybe we buy her a slip?'

'I don't have any money.' Mama gave her standard reply.

I looked over my shoulder to make sure that Nana was not watching me. She was busy writing Uncle Salman a potentially indecipherable letter. Although Nana was knowledgeable, three years of schooling had not been enough. She made plenty of grammatical mistakes, which no one dared to point out to her. Silently, I produced the crumpled five rubles banknote from my pocket and gave it to Mama.

'Where did you get this?'

'I found it on the way back from school.'

The next day, Mama showed me what she had bought. It was a sleeveless knee-length silky slip, the same blue as the

Caspian Sea where we had gone on holidays. The material was soft, and the garment was covered with delicate lace.

'You should give it to her, Gulush. It was your idea. I'll get her some flowers.'

★★★

On Nana's birthday, I woke up extra early and crept into her bed. I was relieved that Nana was by herself. Baba was on a night shift.

'Nana, wake up, I've got something for you.' I shook her gently by the shoulder. 'Happy birthday! Here, unwrap this.'

Groggy, Nana sat up and stared at the present wrapped in the last week's issue of *The Communist Truth* newspaper.

'None of my kids ever bought me presents. You are the light of my eyes. You are the jewel in my crown. You are the beauty of my home.'

'All right, Nana. Look, maybe you won't like it.'

'The present is not so important, it's the attention and love you give me that matters.'

She unfolded the slip.

'It's so beautiful.' Her hard face was softened by a bittersweet smile. 'How did you know that I needed one?'

'Well, you said it the other day…'

'And you remembered? Oh, come here.' She pulled me towards herself and kissed me on top of my head. She smelt all warm and sleepy, her familiar scent clung to my nose even after I moved away from her to admire the present. 'Where did you get the money?'

'I… found it.'

'You did? It's too lovely for me to wear. I'll keep it. It'll always remind me of your love for me.'

'It's not for keeping, Nana, it's for wearing.'

So, she did, on every special occasion she could, but guilt gnawed at me whenever I saw it. I grew to wish she had followed her initial impulse and kept it in a drawer as a memento.

5.

CELEBRATION

Kirovabad, Azerbaijan S.S.R., 1984

Except for the brief respite brought by my birthday present, Nana still spent a lot of time angry or crying, but mostly because of her fights with Uncle Telman. I managed to stay out of their way when they were rowing, except for one time. I had not been quick enough to leave the room before they started. They seemed to have forgotten about me as they argued.

'I will marry her, Mum, whether you want it or not!' Uncle Telman banged his fist hard on the dining table. Plates and glasses, left uncleared after dinner, jingled from the impact of the blow.

'How dare you speak to me like that?' Nana said, her mouth twisted in fury.

'You are forcing me to act like this. How many times do I have to tell you? I'm going to marry Sevil!'

'Don't waste all we've saved for you on this! That money is for your career, your future! So you can look after a family of your own!'

Uncle Telman moved to shout in her face. 'I don't care about my future, without Sevil. I want to marry her!'

Nana became rigid with rage. 'You ungrateful boy. Let's see how far you'll get if I tell your father not to bless your union,' she spat out.

Uncle Telman growled but stayed silent. So, Nana said, 'That family of hers! Whores and gypsies, the lot of them. Decent people won't want to know you! Besides, after what she's done…'

'Enough, Mum. Stop this now.'

Uncle Telman grabbed the large oval table and pushed it with all his force across the room on the polished floor. As the table smashed into the wall, its contents splashed and scattered from floor to ceiling. Nana stood not far from where the table landed. I sat motionless, unable to tear my eyes away from them both.

'Would you rather have me dead like Javan than married to Sevil?' Uncle Telman hissed. Then turned and left, banging the door behind him.

Nana sank silently onto a chair. Her hair was dishevelled, and tears dripped from her chin. She was mumbling something quietly. I edged closer to catch what she was saying. She had started to rock back and forth, her eyes staring ahead. She did not even react when I reached to stroke her greying hair.

I was just gently sweeping the glass and china splinters into the metal dustpan when she suddenly rose from her chair and shuffled towards the phone in the corner of the room. Peering at a piece of paper, she lifted the heavy black receiver and dialled.

'I wish to speak to Sevil,' she said softly. 'It is you? Tell your parents to expect *elchi* tomorrow.'

I could not help but gasp. I knew what *elchi* meant,

though I had no idea yet what it entailed. It was an envoy sent by a groom's family to ask for the bride's hand in marriage. I imagined a delegation of grey-bearded men and possibly old women covered in black scarves marching to Sevil's house and not leaving until her family said 'yes'.

I carried on helping Nana put the living room to rights without speaking of it. It took a long time. Some of Nana's best dishes would now be lining pot plants in the summer. As we rubbed thick brown polish into the table to hide the scratches from Baba, Nana whispered: 'You are such a good girl, Gulush.'

I smiled my best smile at her, and we carried on working. Afterwards, despite the hour, she cooked me sweet pancakes.

★★★

By way of a thank you, I think, I was chosen to accompany my grandparents to Sevil's house, as part of the envoy the next day. Baba wore his best dark navy suit and Nana, the grey dress with the Caspian blue slip I had bought for her birthday with Tarana's money.

Nana gave Sevil's mum a big box of chocolates and a bunch of red carnations, before exchanging hugs and kisses, as if they were already related. We were invited to settle round a table packed with starters. There were large bowls of Russian salad in soured cream and beetroot salad with fresh garlic and walnuts, sitting proudly in the middle of the table, surrounded by large plates of chopped tomatoes, cucumbers, circular slices of salami and feta cheese, pickled cabbage and gherkins. In front of me the scent of fresh tarragon mingled with purple basil and spring onions, competing with the powerful smell of warm flat bread. My mouth watered, but I knew I would have to wait until the hostess served us. So, whilst the adults exchanged pleasantries, I stole quick glances at the big TV.

The Swedish group ABBA were singing 'Mama Mia' on the Russian network. I wished I had fun clothes like them, all satin and sparkles, and not the dull dresses Nana made for me. The blonde singer with straight hair was my favourite because she looked like Sevil.

Baba and Nana did not approve of my interest in ABBA. Baba preferred Azerbaijani folk music, especially *Mugham*, with singers making plaintive noises in their throats, which greatly pleased adults.

The atmosphere lightened when large plates of aromatic *pilau* and steaming *dolma* arrived, the TV was switched off and Baba and Sevil's father, Mahmed *Dayi*, started to drink vodka.

Now it felt like a normal family visit to a relative's house. Baba spoke about our family line, matters of honour and Uncle Telman's education as an engineer. I noted that Sevil was nowhere to be seen; after helping her mother in the kitchen, she disappeared. It was strange that neither Uncle Telman nor his future bride were there to discuss their marriage.

Not a word was mentioned about a wedding.

On the way home, Baba and Nana did not seem happy. Nana said, 'Allah made holes in some people and they think they are women. Even a dog wouldn't eat that *dolma*.'

'Hah,' snorted Baba. 'That Mahmed, what a lightweight. He was drunk at the smell of vodka!'

I suppressed a giggle as Nana nudged him, but I thought they were being unkind, especially since they had not done what they were supposed to do for Uncle Telman. They had not discussed the wedding at all, just ate and drank everything the hosts offered.

I was surprised that when we arrived home, Nana told Uncle Telman that Sevil's family had given their blessing to the marriage. How could I have missed that? I was puzzled until I plucked up the courage to ask Nana about it.

'Silly girl! I thought you knew. They gave us sweet tea!'

She obviously expected me to understand that, though it made no sense. So, I waited until Mama got home and quizzed her. I was not pleased when Mama collapsed into a fit of giggles before answering: 'Didn't you take tea before you left?'

I shook my head. They had not let me have one of the fancy pear-shaped glasses, in case I broke it, I supposed. I had cherry juice compote instead.

'If the answer to the marriage proposal was no, it would have been plain, black tea. But they were given sweet tea and that meant yes! Do they teach you nothing at your school?'

I did not answer. I thought it sounded rather silly and not something a pioneer would need to know.

★★★

A long procession of cars decorated with red ribbons and flowers crawled along the street, as all the drivers leaned on their horns. Squashed in the back seat of Baba's car with Mama and her cousins, I craned my neck in a vain attempt to breathe some fresh air through the open windows. The short journey left my armpits damp, while Mama and the three cousins carefully dabbed their faces with handkerchiefs to keep their heavy make-up intact. My heart fluttered with excitement, especially at the thought of seeing Sevil's wedding dress.

As I climbed out of the car, I licked my dry, salty lips. We were immediately behind a white four-door GAZ-24 Volga that Uncle Telman had borrowed from a relative. The car's bumper was decorated with a doll in a wedding dress, fresh flowers and lots of ribbons that stretched from the front of the car all the way to the back. Uncle Telman was unusually twitchy. He kept pulling down the sleeves of his smart grey suit, freeing his neck from the starchy collar of a white shirt and the stranglehold of a stripy tie.

Drops of sweat glistened on Uncle Salman's forehead when he emerged from the GAZ-24 to stand solemnly by his brother's side. Looking at Uncle Salman's smart clothes, no one could guess that he had arrived the night before in a sweat-caked military uniform with stinky *portyankas*, giant bandages he had to wear inside his rubber boots instead of socks. I was not sure what was the more exciting: to see my older uncle marry or have my younger uncle back home for a week.

The courtyard in front of Sevil's building looked like a disturbed ants' nest. Neighbours were filing out of the five-storey building to gape at the groom and his family. Escorted by a crowd of voluptuous female relatives, my two uncles went into Sevil's flat and I elbowed adults' thick thighs and wide waistlines to have a good look at what was happening indoors.

Fully made-up and looking delicate, Sevil resembled the doll on the bumper of the GAZ-24. Her eyebrows were plucked thinner, the sign that she was not a single woman anymore. My sightline was abruptly cut when the crowd parted to let a man through.

It was Nana's brother, Great Uncle Hussein. His bald head must have been baking underneath his big, woolly, Mullah hat. His small eyes, encircled with wrinkles, peered out above a large nose. His fleshy lips, which seemed always to be pursed and resembled a hen's bottom, gave him an unhappy expression. As he reached the couple, he opened a black leather-bound Koran and started to read a prayer in a sing-song tone. His face brightened slightly with the flash of his two gold teeth.

I knew Uncle Hussein lived in mountainous Dashkasan with Arpen, his Armenian wife, and the daughter from her first marriage. Nana disapproved of his choices – to marry a divorcee with a child who was also an Armenian... There was still tension around that subject, but Nana had often told me why she still loved him so much.

Great Uncle Hussein was Nana's only immediate family. She was barely ten and her brother fifteen when their revolutionary mother died. Nana spoke of her with pride, how her mother had wielded a gun and refused to cover her head. She only had one memory of her father and that was tainted with regret. He had finally returned from exile in Siberia, for political activism, when she was eight. He brought her a simple present of coloured pencils, but in disappointment and confusion she had broken every one of them in a display of temper I would have never dared to express. He was deported to Iran by Stalin's administration shortly after, all because his surname ended -zadeh, a sign of some Iranian heritage. She never saw him again and for all she knew she had half-siblings across the river Araz in Iran.

After her mother's death, Nana was forced to move to Kirovabad to live with her mother's cousin. When World War Two began, Nana had just turned eleven. She had to quit school and start working at a match factory to support her widowed 'aunt' and her two young children. This woman used the small bread ration Nana brought home daily for herself, and let Nana starve.

Somehow the news reached Great Uncle Hussein, who was newly enlisted into the Soviet Army to fight in the Second World War. Risking death, he went AWOL to bring Nana some food. He was severely punished for that, but Nana had never forgotten this kind gesture. Every time they fell out, she reconciled with him out of gratitude for his love at the time when she was only eleven.

The reading from the Koran was long. I lost interest in the spectacle but trying to leave the flat proved as difficult as squeezing in. Even when I got outside, the smell of perfume mixed with sweat lingered in my nostrils.

As people started filing out of the flat, musicians greeted them with *Vagzali*, a traditional solemn wedding tune. Mama and several of her cousins lifted their arms, curving them at the wrists, and danced, the swift moves of their high-heeled shoes raising billows of dust from the ground. Uncle Telman and Sevil were chaperoned to the car by a procession of relatives. Before they climbed in, a lamb was sacrificed at their feet to ward off the 'evil eye'. The man who held the lamb was quick, shedding its blood at the couple's feet before I could look away. Sevil's wedding dress remained impeccably white.

Once they were in the car, it began to move away from the crowd. The sound of music was replaced by a cacophony of car horns, honking. The guests headed to our house, where a giant military marquee was erected on the street.

I had to walk home with the older relatives and pretended not to be listening to their gossip whenever they glanced at me. Talk was centred on Sevil's henna party of the night before. I caught half-sentences about 'private' things but did not understand what they were talking about.

Our street looked like a big car park with guests parking randomly in the middle of the road, given that the marquee blocked off the traffic for the day. The sound of a nagara, a traditional wooden-based drum, greeted us long before we could see or hear the other musicians. Those playing stringed instruments and singing folk songs were struggling to compete with the nagara and the car horns of guests arriving.

Anxious not to miss a beat, I made my way into the epicentre of the dancing crowd. The sharp, rapid moves of the dancers, combined with booming music, left my ears and heart pounding. Uncle Telman and Sevil soon glided gracefully into the marquee and took their places at the top table, which was on a podium.

As soon as the guests were seated, a line of young men appeared with large dishes of food: kebabs, pilau and *kalapir*, which were placed on the tables. I looked around to ask where I could sit and eat, but Mama and Nana were nowhere to be seen. Although ordinarily I was delighted to be left alone, on this occasion I just felt left out.

I spotted Nana walking from pan to pan in the front garden, giving instructions to cooks, sampling food and bossing waiters around. She looked too busy to talk to me, so I returned to the marquee. The music was blaring loudly. Several men were dancing. Some seemed clumsy, stumbling over and into one another.

Mama was leaning against the top table, which was piled with food, untouched. As was the custom, Sevil sat sombrely, eyes downcast, whilst Uncle Telman was like a grand statue. The entertainment was for the extended family and friends, not the couple.

People would periodically approach the table to have their photo taken with the bride and groom. Rolling his broad shoulders back, Uncle Telman would stand stiffly next to Sevil and Mama, posing gravely for the photos. Not a shadow of a smile passed any lips.

They were obviously busy too, so I went to loiter by the pans, some nearly as tall as me, and I was nine! Eventually, Svetlana *Khala*, a wife of Mama's cousin, who had two daughters of my age, gave me a plateful of pilau – steamed rice coloured yellow and light brown with saffron, turmeric and cinnamon. It came with gooey caramelised onions coating tender lamb, chestnuts, jumbo raisins and soft apricots, which slid easily down my throat. Even after a big portion I could have eaten more but was ordered to help wash up. I worked until my legs throbbed and the guests disappeared into the late night.

Relieved, I went upstairs and gathered my school uniform, schoolbag and pyjamas. I felt disappointed that the wedding had turned out to be more work than fun, but I was still hoping for some giggles as I headed for the back door.

'Where are you going?' Mama's voice startled me.

'Over to Sevil's,' I said confidently. 'She promised that when she got married to Uncle Telman, I could stay with her.'

Mama started really laughing for the first time that day.

'You can't stay there tonight.' She chuckled. 'It's their first night… you need to give them some time. Now, go to bed. You have got school tomorrow.'

I went away sadly and put myself to bed, but all sorts of noises were coming from outside: from loud clangs to chatting and tinkling. Clearing up after three hundred guests was a big job, performed by the entire community. Relatives and neighbours came to do anything that needed to be done: wash plates, scrub big pans, sort out cutlery, clean floors, stack up chairs, take the giant military marquee down, dish leftovers and take them to neighbours, rinse out and hang tea towels. The list of tasks was endless, and people did them without any grudges. It was a favour, to be returned one day. My family helped our relatives and neighbours all the time. Nana could easily cook for two to three hundred people at weddings and funerals, and was asked to do so, at least once every couple of months.

I shut my eyes tightly, wishing for some quiet so that I could fall asleep. It had been a long day. Why hadn't Mama let me sleep at Sevil's? The last time I'd seen her properly was two hours earlier, when she stepped through the front gates and a plate was placed on the ground by the entrance. Sevil held Uncle Telman's arm and tried to break the plate with the heel of her shoe. The bride's temperament in family life was judged by whether she could break the plate or not. If a bride broke the plate, it showed she'd be feisty. If she could not crack it at all, she was probably a cold fish. The plate cracked ever so slightly under Sevil's pointy heel. Oh, she would be the best, I was confident.

Then I heard the bedroom door creak open.

'Come in, Arpen,' Nana said in a half-whisper. 'Give me a minute.'

I heard her tiptoe into my room to check I was asleep, so I stayed very still, knowing she'd be cross if I was still awake.

Satisfied, Nana crept out, leaving the door ajar and spoke to Arpen in hushed tones: 'When I asked you to be Telman and Sevil's *yenge*, I hoped I could count on your discretion. It's the honour of the whole family which is at stake here. Obviously, even Hussein shouldn't know anything about this. There is no need to watch them tonight. We know the outcome.'

'What are you saying, Rosa…?' Arpen sounded breathless. 'She's not a virgin?'

'It's worse than that. Our honour is in your hands.'

'Are you telling me that she's preg…?'

'Shhhh! She was. I'm afraid so,' Nana replied. 'She let Telman into her flat when her parents were away. I paid for the… you know… I took her to the best specialist. I just hope she can get pregnant again. I promised to sacrifice a lamb if she bears his child.'

'I wondered why you chose me,' said Arpen. 'I haven't met any other Armenian *yenge* in my life.'

'You're my family.' Nana's voice was tense.

'Of course, Rosa, your family's honour is my honour. I just can't believe you let him marry her! Sevil should wash your feet and drink the water. Incredible generosity.'

'Yes. That girl should be indebted to me for the rest of her life. I saved her from such disgrace.'

'It's true. Anyway, I'd better go. People expect me to be outside their bedroom door now. Don't worry, I'll do what needs to be done. A bloodied sheet will be displayed when we celebrate their union in three days' time.'

'Thank you, Arpen, I won't forget this,' said Nana, seeing her to the door.

I lay in my bed, trying to make sense of what I had just overheard. Although I did not understand most of it, I thought perhaps it explained the row that Nana had had with Uncle Telman when he damaged the table.

6.

NEWS

After the wedding, I spent most of my free time with Sevil. As soon as I was back from school and she returned from her morning shifts at the local pharmacy, I would follow her around like a puppy. I watched her cook hearty meals for Uncle Telman, giddy from the smell of spiced meat and the stories of her childhood in Berlin. Sometimes, while a marinated lamb leg, stuffed with garlic cloves, baked in the oven, I watched Russian comedies with her. I loved the way, unlike anyone else in my family, she laughed out loud at the mishaps of my favourite Russian actor Andrey Mironov in *Unbelievable Adventures of Italians in Russia*, *The Diamond Arm* and *The Twelve Chairs*. Mironov's irresistible charm, witticism and musicality appealed to Sevil as much as it won my heart too.

Although she cooked Uncle Telman elaborate meals, Sevil hardly ate anything herself. I had even heard her being sick. However, when Nana bought a sheep to be sacrificed in our back garden, I remembered the conversation I had overheard the night of the wedding, and realised Sevil must be pregnant. Having been allowed to pet the animal all morning I was upset when Uncle Telman cut and skinned it in front of my eyes. I was confused as to what to do when it was served up as kebabs for tea. Cooked on iron skewers over charcoal, the aromatic meat proved irresistible and tasted delicious, but I did feel sorry for the sheep. From that day, the household filled with a sense of expectation. I eagerly awaited my new cousin.

As the due date approached, Sevil struggled with the heat. The late June sun was relentless and, by eight in the morning, even with all the windows and doors open to create a draft, their bungalow felt like an oven. Sevil's legs swelled up and looked like two white tree trunks. She spent most of her time lounging on her bed. I joined her as often as I was allowed, bringing her cold compote drinks that Nana made, boiling water with added sugar and seasonal fruit. Sometimes I would cut up lemons for her. Licking my fingers afterwards I marvelled how she could possibly eat something that sour.

I did not know how the birth went because the grown-ups drove her to the hospital, leaving me home with Amaliya *Khala*, our next-door neighbour. Impatient to greet my new cousin, I paced around the front garden until Nana returned to announce that Sevil and baby Aisha left to stay at her parents' for two months.

Scratching my back that night, Mama explained that it was the custom for the grandmother to care for her daughter and her grandchild, but I hated that I had to entertain myself with only the clucking chickens.

★★★

My daily boredom was cut short by the return of Uncle Salman from his military conscription in Crimea. We all gathered one afternoon, friends and family, for a meal, eager to hear as much as possible about the past two years. Still in his military uniform, his stubbly, now grown-up face stretched into a smile, he recounted anecdote after anecdote. He ate at the same time, occasionally pausing to wipe lamb liquor from his lips.

'I know you want to hear everything about everything.' Uncle Salman looked around his eager audience. 'But most things are—' he lowered his voice— 'top secret.' It sounded very mysterious and important. We all nodded to show we understood. His infectious laugh filled the room. 'I'm joking! There isn't that much to tell about the military service. I worked in the kitchen and stayed out of trouble. However,' he said, sitting up straight, 'I can tell you about how Dad behaved when he came to visit me! It happened like this…

'So… we decided to go on a ferry-ride and Dad bought two tickets… except I managed to lose them. Of course, he told me off for that. Then we set out to look for them. Easier said than done, given that you can't see the ground – there are so many people in that port. Nose to the ground, I'm frantically looking for them when, suddenly, I hear this painfully familiar voice. I look up and see it's Dad. He's climbed up on Lenin's statue and he's shouting, "People. If you see two tickets on the ground, they're mine"!'

A roar of laughter followed, which warmed me from the inside out. Uncle Salman had a special way of recounting anecdotes about his adventures with Baba when he visited him in Crimea. Maybe it was the way his eyes twinkled with mischief when he was telling stories and the way he embodied his horror and embarrassment at Baba's lack of self-consciousness or perhaps it was the fact that he was unusually talkative today. I wondered whether all those gathered around the dining table were laughing so much because everyone was drunk with happiness at Uncle Salman's return. It also helped that Baba was at work now, so even my uncles were relaxed.

'Gulush.' Mama motioned me towards the kitchen.

I did not want to move. Though the stories were funny, and I wanted to stay, I stood up dutifully and went to see what the problem was.

To my surprise, she said: 'Let's go for a walk.'

'What about Uncle Salman?' I protested.

'Not even Nana will notice we're out just now,' she insisted. Her tone was urgent. She was already clutching her handbag, ready to leave.

Normally I would have been first out the door, but that day I followed her reluctantly.

She took me two bus rides away, to Lenin's Park. Once there, I could not think why I'd objected to come. The earthy air made my heart swell. We walked under the ancient oak trees and giant conifers in silence. No one else was about. We used to come to this park with Avaz when I was little but, these days, it was a rare treat. I pushed out the memory of Mama's bloodied wrists and lingered behind to gather some dandelions and daisies.

'I'm going to ask you something but, before I do, you must promise not to tell anyone else,' Mama said as I extended her a small bouquet. She ran her fingers through her thick black hair as she always did when she was nervous before accepting the white and yellow bunch from me.

'Of course, Mama, you can trust me.'

I felt like an over-tuned violin string, my intuition sensed she was about to say something really important. I peered at her face, concerned how whatever it was might come to affect me.

'Do you still want me to get married again?' She spoke quickly, then looked away.

'I do,' I said. 'Yes. I want you to be happy. When are you getting married?'

I thought it strange she kept her eyes on the ground, as if studying her black heels, rather than facing me.

We were by the park gates by then. I pulled her to a stop and put my face between hers and the ground: 'Mama, what is it? What do you have to tell me?' I spoke to her as if she were the child.

I drew closer, in the hope of catching her eye.

'This is the part that no one should know about.' She paused. 'It's tomorrow. I am getting married tomorrow,' she said, finally looking into my eyes.

I gasped. Into my mind rushed all the things there would be to do. What would I wear? What would we eat? What would she wear? Her next words dashed all those thoughts away.

'Listen to me. You're the only person who knows this. I am trusting you not to tell anyone,' she said. Her body was trembling, but her eyes were firm.

'Will you ever tell them?' I managed to squeak. How long could I keep such a thing to myself?

'Of course, I will. Once we register our marriage, there's nothing they can do about it. Jalil and I have planned it all.'

So, it was to be Jalil. I relaxed a bit. I knew about Jalil.

Several weeks before this, Mama had started coming home late, complaining that renovations at the museum were disrupting her work, but she soon had to confide in me.

I met him when I visited her at the museum. He was one of the decorators from Baku. Tall and skinny with slightly stooping shoulders and uneven, smoke-stained teeth, he wasn't much to look at, but he seemed quiet and gentle. He had the same dark skin and black hair as Mama, so they looked good together, but also like they were cousins. Mama obviously liked him.

It had become just like it had been with Avaz. I was the third party in their relationship. Whether walking home together or staying after hours at the museum, I kept their meetings secret.

Why was she still looking away from me now?

She let me hug her excitedly then we started for home. My head bubbled again, this time with visions of what would happen after the marriage. We would be a proper family and have our own home where I could invite friends. He might even let me wear trousers. I wanted to share all my thoughts with Mama, but as usual she shushed me.

'We don't want anyone to tell Nana, do we?' she whispered on the first bus, handing me back a slightly withered bouquet she had been clutching since the park. 'You never know who is around. Just a few hours more…' She took my hand in hers. '… and then…'

I smiled conspiratorially.

'What shall I wear?' I asked.

'You can't come, I'm afraid. It's a school day. We only need two witnesses, and they have to be grown-ups.'

I bit my lip in.

'But there will be plenty of time for special celebrations afterwards. We can celebrate for the rest of our lives.'

Satisfied with this answer, I settled back against her and began to count the lampposts along the darkening road. I felt so close to her then.

★★★

I do not remember much about the marriage ceremony day. I know I could not concentrate at school and that Mama came to pick me up, with Jalil, wearing a fine, green velvet dress. I hugged them both. We went home happily, but I do not think they even let him through the door.

After that, I remember Nana waving her arms and showering Mama in curses. Mama, who had looked so beautiful, ended up looking as drooping, dishevelled and out of place as the small bouquet of wildflowers I had picked her the day before.

It took a long while for the dust to settle. Nana refused to speak to Mama. She would only communicate with her through me. Caught between two fires, I knew I was going to be burnt whatever I did. Mama and Jalil had to live apart to start with. There was no space for Mama and me in the small room Jalil was currently renting, so, despite the friction, we were allowed to stay put. Jalil was clearly not welcome in our house.

Nana was astonished when she received a message saying Jalil's family would like to visit, but convention meant she could not refuse them. As Mama had predicted, any objections to the marriage had to be set aside.

'What is done, is done,' Nana said, though the

atmosphere between mother and daughter remained cool. They were forced to converse about the many practicalities of preparing for such an event – how many kilos of meat to order, who should be invited, what should we wear and so on – but kept these interactions limited.

The next two weeks passed quickly. The day before the guests were due to arrive, the drawing room was ready, and the house had been spring cleaned. Thirty guests were to attend the meal, which Nana and Mama prepared with a clutch of friends and relatives.

When Amir *Dayi*, Jalil's dad, arrived with his two daughters for a three-day visit, everyone put on a happy face. They greeted them like close relatives. Tall and stooping, like Jalil, Amir *Dayi* was quiet and reserved. His brown eyes, looking out from under the greying, bushy eyebrows, seemed to be kind. He did not talk much but was happy to respond if someone initiated conversation. His two daughters, Emiliya and Afag, talked like schoolteachers, but they were pleasant and friendly.

Jalil's mother, however, had refused to come. I could sense the air of animosity that her absence created: Jalil was her only son and six years younger than Mama, who already had me. It was known that Amir *Dayi* had had other plans for him. Jalil's family were obviously trying to find the best in the situation, so reluctantly my grandparents gave their tacit consent to the union.

As was the custom, every evening for three days, relatives and neighbours came to pay their respects to the newlyweds and their families. As far as the outside world was concerned, Mama and Jalil's official marriage coincided with the family gatherings. There was nothing grand about this celebration: no big marquee outside like we had for Uncle Telman and Sevil's wedding. Mama did not get a white dress, but I was excited, for now the world knew, I thought we would soon be moving into our own home.

My favourite part of those three days was the quiet of the evenings before bedtime. Jalil's sister, Emiliya played the most enchanting music I had ever heard. I would sit nearby yearning to join in on my violin but did not dare to voice my desire. She was playing traditional Azerbaijani songs, like Ala Gozlum, whose tunes I did not know because at music school, as Baba had said, we only studied the 'so-called classics', most of them 'relics of decadent capitalism'. As I sat behind her, watching her long fingers skimming over the keys of the old piano, breathing in the sweet scent of her perfume, I remembered my first introduction to the violin when I was five.

After months of me being able to point out her private pupils' mistakes every time when they hit the wrong key, Mama had decided to take me to the music school where she worked. A tall Russian woman tested my aptitude by asking me to repeat a series of claps and stomps that she showed me. It seemed a strange way to find out whether I had any musical talent because there was no music involved, but I replicated every move and sound she made. As I did so, I noticed she raised her eyebrows and shot a glance at Mama. She offered sequence after sequence to me. I realised now she was checking to make sure my performance was not just a fluke. At the time I just enjoyed the attention.

'What instrument do you want to play?' I remember how the teacher bent down and peered into my face.

'She's only five, she can't start for another three years,' Mama said, coming to my rescue.

'Nonsense, my dear Mariyam. With a talent like this she can start today. I recommend she try the violin.'

Now Mama was surprised.

'How will she cope with music theory? She is still learning to read and write.'

'No problem. You can attend those classes with her and take notes to discuss with her later.'

At the time I did not want a violin, or any music theory classes. Still my family bought me a violin as soon as they could. It was the smallest available. Nana made me a little red pillow to tie under my chin for the instrument to rest upon to keep my posture straight. In no time, I started to attend classes at the music school. Although I loved my teacher, Kima Shamirovna, the truth was that what I really wanted to do was to play the piano, like Mama.

Watching Emiliya's performance on our piano had reignited that longing, especially given that since she started her job at the museum Mama had stopped playing piano almost entirely.

★★★

The day after the wedding guests left, I was unbuckling my sandals in the hall when I heard Mama and Nana speaking in hushed voices. Intrigued, I silently drew closer to eavesdrop. The door into the living room was ajar, and I realised that Mama and Nana were actually sitting next to each other.

'Maryam, you can trust me,' Nana said. Her voice sounded more loving than I had ever heard it before.

74

'But Mum…' Mama's voice sounded troubled.

'Be sensible, Maryam. You have no idea what conditions are like there. You don't even know where you will be living.' Nana shuffled closer to Mama. 'Besides, she will always be your daughter.'

They were talking about me!

'That's true,' replied Mama. 'So, she should be with me. We do know where we'll stay, in Jalil's sister's flat, until we find a place of our own to rent.'

'You hardly know her, and you don't know her family. Are you sure there's enough space? Gulush can't sleep with you two. She's ten. She'll need her own space. Can they offer her that?'

'I don't really know,' Mama replied, 'but we'll manage somehow. She can sleep on the floor.'

In the dark hallway, I nodded my head. I wanted to cry out that of course I could sleep on the floor, even a bare floor, as long as I was with Mama.

'Well, I think there are too many unknowns.' Nana's voice had started to sound firmer now. 'The move will disrupt her schooling, just when she's doing so well.'

'Yes, yes,' Mama said. 'But I don't even know how long we might stay in Latvia.'

Latvia? Mama was leaving the country? Without me? My eyes filled with tears.

'She will always be your daughter,' Nana repeated. 'And we will come and visit in the summer,' she added as an afterthought.

I thought of the lush green leaves of the trees in the garden. This summer had not ended yet. Nana was talking about a visit next year? I was shaking with shock now.

'And remember… Jalil is not her father. As far as she is concerned, he is a stranger to her. Look how developed she is already. It's not right for them to share a room.'

'Enough, Mum,' Mama sighed. 'I'll let her stay behind,' she said, and hung her head.

'You've made the right decision,' Nana said. She patted Mama's hand and passed her a handkerchief.

After all she had promised me… I felt so betrayed and alone as I crept up to the bedroom. Trying not to cry, I spread my homework out on the bed, so that when Mama came up, I was able to pretend I was too busy to talk just then. They had not asked me what I wanted. I did not know what to say, so I chose silence.

★★★

When Mama broke the news to me later that day, I felt like she was already gone. Determined not to let my true feelings show, the only response she got was a shrug of my shoulders before I got up to lay the table for tea, as if nothing had happened.

Mama came to school with me the next day and told Bahar Rahimovna, the lead teacher for my class, about her imminent move to Latvia. They had a long conversation, during which Mama embarrassed me by pleading that my teacher look out for me. I found it awkward when at the end of the conversation Bahar Rahimovna promised to do her best, then ruffled my hair as if I were a pet.

It hurt when Mama and Jalil left for Latvia. Quickly, my life began to settle into a new pattern: school, home, violin lessons, helping Nana with chores, missing Mama…

school, home, violin lessons, chores, missing Mama…
school, home, violin lessons, missing Mama, missing
Mama, missing Mama, missing…

7.

VICTORY DAY

Kirovabad, Azerbaijan S.S.R., 1986

While Mama was away, I found much comfort in being with Kima Shamirovna, my music teacher. She held my classes in her house in The Red Village, a part of the city with a predominantly Armenian population. It was slightly further than the music school, but it meant there was no pressure to rush to and from home when my class had ended. I could sit and have a snack or play a game with her, waiting for Baba to collect me by car.

I loved Kima Shamirovna and wanted to express that in a poem I wrote for her on her birthday on 7th November. This was a memorable date as we always had a large military parade that day to celebrate the October Revolution of 1917 when the Bolsheviks came to power. Walking back from the parade, the lines of a poem had already floated through my mind, and I could hardly wait to reach home so that I could commit them to paper.

The seventh of November is the red page on the calendar
To celebrate the massacre

Of Tsar and its regime.
But for me this day is special
Because it's my favourite teacher's birthday,
Perhaps we could sit together
With a boiling samovar and the largest cake,
Laughing and cheering,
To mark this day.

I never showed the poem to Kima Shamirovna as I felt too embarrassed to display my love for her so openly. Instead, keeping it a secret from everyone, I submitted it to the *Pioneer's Truth* newspaper, published across the entire Soviet Union. They sent me an encouraging letter, with suggestions on how to improve on it, to make it more patriotic, the letter said.

The day after I received the feedback from the editorial board of the *Pioneer's Truth*, Uncle Salman caught me off-guard, re-reading the letter and smiling to myself. He snatched it from my hand thinking it was a love letter from some boy.

'You call this a poem? Pfff,' he said.

He seemed relieved that I was not doing something stupid like Mama used to and lost interest in the letter. I binned it. It took me a long time to recover from his sneering words.

★★★

Despite Uncle Salman's reaction, months later, I still liked the poem. It comforted me somehow. I mentally recited it again as I waited with my class to join the military march of the Victory Day Parade on 9th May.

The thought of Kima Shamirovna kept me warm on that chilly morning. The march was my least favourite of the three largest military parades that we had to attend every year. It commemorated the end of the Great Patriotic War, when Nazi Germany capitulated in 1945. I preferred the celebration of Workers' Day on 1st May. Eight days before, we had stood on the pavement watching the colourful and joyous parade. It signified the start of summer. This meant I could wear a short-sleeved white shirt and navy skirt instead of my dull brown long-sleeved dress, with its lace collar and black pinafore. Although the weather was often colder than I hoped, I never complained, because Nana might refuse to buy me an ice cream.

Today, on Bahar Rahimovna's cue, our class joined the flow of people on Lenin Avenue. Waving my arms in perfect rhythm with the *rechetka*, I held my head high and my posture straight, making my moves deliberate and precise. Bahar Rahimovna shouted commands from time to time, though the murmur of the crowd on the pavement often drowned her delicate voice.

I wished I was watching so I could see the whole spectacle: the musicians with cymbals and trumpets, the veterans shining with medals and the massed ranks of pioneers with our red scarves flickering like flames from our necks in the breeze. I thought it had to be more fun to watch than to take part.

I tried to squash these thoughts by reminding myself that it was, as our teacher said, an honour to be part of the Victory Day parade. So many people laid down their lives for us in World War II. This reprimand did not work for long. My legs were aching and there was no chance to rest.

Whilst the people cheered, we marched, and I fantasised about how I would get an ice cream after the parade.

Again and again, we had to shout our *rechetka*:

'One, two, three, four,
Here comes our pioneer squad!'

My thoughts began to drift further away, to my new little brother. His photo had arrived in the post two days before. I could not stop admiring it. He was chubby and cute, the image of his parents, with dark hair and complexion.

I was so deep in my daydream that I nearly bumped into the back of the child in front of me as the procession suddenly stopped. The sea of people stirred, like gentle waves lapping by the shore, but we were not allowed to chat or relax yet, and now we were stopped under a large oak tree. I shivered. The sunlight, filtering through the branches heavy with bursting buds, was robbed of its warmth. By the time the procession started to move again, I was chilled to the bone, but I managed to continue to walk, robot-like in time to the music. My mind drifted again as I wondered whether Great Uncle Hussein would come to see us that day.

Great Uncle Hussein was a war veteran with so many medals you could hardly see the front of his brown suit jacket. Some years, on this day, Nana would make an extra effort for him. I had mixed feelings about his visits. He may have been Nana's closest relative, but they often ended up fighting over what seemed like trivial things.

I was only six months old when they had had their biggest one, but knew the legend of it by heart, since Nana had told it to me so many times. We had come to stay at Great Uncle Hussein's house in the mountains because I was unwell, and the doctor had recommended fresh air. Nana came loaded with a huge amount of provisions to share, including homemade clotted cream, fresh lamb, honey, vegetables, fruit and herbs, but within an hour they had a terrible fight and Nana said she would leave.

For Nana, to drag all that food back home would have been as painful as leaving it. She was so angry. Before her brother could stop her, she heaved the bags to the window, which opened over a mountain cliff, hurled all her gifts out one by one, then wrapped me up in my shawl and left. Great Uncle Hussein was yet to do anything that dramatic – he never brought any gifts – but his presence, despite the fights, broke up the day-to-day monotony of my life at that time.

No one at home had time for me, so I enjoyed listening to all his war stories on quiet afternoons. He told me once: 'Water was so precious during the war. The Germans knew this and used it against us. You know how to get water from a well?'

I nodded. I had seen it on TV.

'So, the bucket went down to the bottom, you filled it up, turned the handle to get it back up and *Kerboom*!' He swooped his arms up so quickly I nearly fell off my chair. 'That was that.'

I never knew for certain if it had happened to him personally, or if he had witnessed such, but Nana had told me that a bomb had once exploded near to him and given him severe concussion.

A change of pace and the start of another song swept me back into the present of the parade and seeing where we were, I realised that it was nearly over. Just a few more steps and cheers later, we all saluted at attention, then were dismissed.

Buses were not operating yet because there were still too many people on the roads, but the pavements had cleared surprisingly quickly. Sadly, this meant that the street-sellers promptly packed up and left too. Disappointed at missing out on my ice cream, I went to a nearby shop and bought a slice of baklava. The pastry felt stodgy and tasted stale, but I was past caring. At least it provided some temporary comfort and relief.

As I munched it, on my way to find a bus, my baby brother's face flashed into my mind again. Did they have baklava like Nana made in Latvia? Could I take him some when I went to meet him in the holidays?

My trip with Nana to Latvia was by far the best experience of my life: Jalil taught me to ride his bicycle, so I spent most days at the playground with other children. In Kirovabad we had no playgrounds at all and not a single girl I knew, myself included, had a bike. Spending time with Mama and Jalil was fun, especially as they tried to show me and Nana the best local attractions. Mama kept fainting because of her pregnancy, but we had exciting days out. The best one was visiting a live aquarium, with amazing fishes and animals that I had only seen before on television. In Kirovabad, the museum where Mama used to work was probably the only local attraction and hardly anyone visited it anyway.

When the bus came it was half-empty. I had my five gapiks ready for the fare. The parade had finished only two stops from home, so although my legs ached, I decided to stand near the exit.

As I watched the driver pass the steering wheel between his rough fingers, I heard a slight noise of footsteps down the bus. Someone had come to stand uncomfortably close behind me. I could smell his stinking breath tickling the hairs on the back of my neck. I had seen men rub up against women on the bus before. I usually travelled on full buses and chose my seat carefully. My face flushing, I shifted closer to the door. Suddenly the man's arm slid under my armpit to rest on my breast. I felt myself freeze, not knowing how to react, what to do. I think the driver saw but he frowned and looked away, shaking his head. A girl alone on a bus – he had made his judgement, despite my uniform. The grey littered pavements of Lenin Avenue whizzed by as my fear grew. The hand started to work on a button, and the man pressed in closer. If I moved, I might attract people's attention, who were likely to react like the driver. Nana always said it was the woman's fault when she attracted unwanted male attention. Wondering what I had done, I stayed still and quiet, waiting for my stop as the hand continued to fiddle with my button. When the bus doors opened, I lunged forward, breaking away from the disgusting hands and pelted down the streets, tears flying from my face.

No one had followed me, but I did not stop running until I reached our home. Breathless and broken, I slammed the iron gates against the hated world of that invasion. With my sweaty shirt clinging to my skin, I vaulted soundlessly up to my bedroom to peel off my clothes. I sponged myself down with cold water, dried myself with a towel, put on fresh clothes and tried to calm my breathing to stop myself crying.

If Nana saw me, I knew she would be angry again, because I would not be able to tell her what had really happened. She would think it was about Mama. The few times she'd caught me crying after Mama had left, she had gone into a rage and shouted at me for 'betraying her'.

'All the effort I have taken, raising you as my own, and yet you still pine for a mother who couldn't care less about you!' she had said.

In my heart I did not believe that was true. Mama might have a new son with Jalil, but I heard her say myself that I would always be her daughter.

I picked up a magazine and fanned my face to help reduce the puffiness around my eyes. No, I could never tell Nana what had happened. She always blamed Mama if something went wrong with men. She would blame me. I flicked through the magazine to distract my mind and stem further tears. It was a 1986 copy of *Rabotniza*, The Women Worker, first published in 1923. Over the years, Mama had told me, the front covers had changed a lot, from grim drawings in black and red to more pleasing ones, but there were still inspiring stories of Soviet women, alongside household and other advice. This one had a beautiful short blonde-haired girl sitting peacefully on a hilltop looking at a dragonfly in her hand. She looked a bit like I used to, so I imagined it was me sitting there. As my breathing slowed and deepened, I realised my throat was sore. I sat there for as long as I dared.

Emerging from the bedroom, I was relieved to hear Lev Leshenko belting out 'Den Pobedi' on the television. When I entered the living room, I could see him, handsome, though in his forties, head held high, singing with pathos and conviction his song about the Victory Parade. Inspired, I went towards Nana and kissed her on the head.

'Chop and fry three onions. Then add them to the mashed potatoes,' she said. 'I'm making *pirozhki* for dinner,' she said, pulling her headscarf tighter over her greying hair.

Though my still tightly knotted stomach rejected the thought of food, I plodded to the kitchen. Maybe my eyes would return to looking normal by the time Nana had finished watching the transmission of a parade on Red Square. I was glad to be alone in the kitchen because my hands shook as I chopped the large onions, which stung my eyes. Perhaps that could be my excuse to Nana, if she noticed anything... I was crying because of the onions. Their smell, as they sizzled in the butter, was strangely comforting, though inside I was still reliving the incident on the bus. I had never thought such a thing would happen to me.

As Nana entered the kitchen, I grabbed the bowl of mashed potatoes and turned to stir in the fried onions. She stooped over the sink in her frayed cotton dress, to wash her hands, her back to me.

'Get out the flour, salt and yogurt now.'

She mixed the raising agent, which stunk like mouldy cheese to my nose. Then added it, an egg and some yogurt to the flour and started to knead it with her wrinkled hands into a dough.

'How was the parade?' she said, lowering herself onto her creaky wooden chair. She started to make small dough balls.

'Great,' I said.

As I filled a pan with sunflower oil, I had to fight back

my tears again. I was surprised, but thankful, that she did not ask for more details. She too seemed to have something on her mind. Silently we worked together. Nana stuffed the dough with the onioned mash, pinching them into parcels at each corner with practiced precision. I fried them in batches in the smouldering oil.

When golden-brown, I piled the *pirozhki* on a large platter. Nana had a mix of salt and pepper ready on her faded plate. She dunked each one before gnashing it with her yellowed false teeth. She did not seem to notice that I only managed one for her four. Usually, she would press me to have more. I started to feel uneasy. Everyone knew this silence before the storm tactic Nana used. Perhaps she had heard me come in after all.

'Your mother is returning.' Nana's eyes felt like two leeches trying to suck out my emotions.

From somewhere inside, I found the strength to say: 'It will be nice for us to have a baby about. Won't it, Nana?' as I calmly reached for another *pirozhki* and dunked it in her seasoning.

8.

RETURN

Kirovabad, Azerbaijan S.S.R., 1987

I packed my violin away after my class finished and sat at a round table in Kima Shamirovna's guest room to wait for Baba. This was my favourite part of the day. Sometimes we would even play a boardgame, one with colourful crystals. Baba was often late. Kima Shamirovna offered me her own homemade *pirozhki*, baked in the oven, Armenian style, rather than fried, and quizzed me about Mama.

'What is it like to have your mum back?'

'Amazing,' I said, accepting the warm golden pastry from my music teacher.

'We'll have to impress your mum at the exam this year, won't we?' she said, pushing the greying curls from over her knowing eyes.

I nodded vigorously. Unusually, Kima Shamirovna and I were going to perform a duet for the end of year exam. Having her on stage with me ramped up the pressure, I thought. I had overheard her telling a colleague the piece was normally only taught at the senior conservatoire. Before I could continue fretting about the exam, Kima

Shamirovna interrupted my thoughts. Pointing at my hand, she said, 'Is that one from your mum?'

'Yes, isn't it lovely?' I gushed. 'It's real gold. The purple stone in the middle is an amethyst, for healing. I have to be careful with it. It's a flower, can you see? The gold petals are very delicate.'

She held my hand to admire it. Her hands were soft as snowflakes, with the fine, strong fingers of a musician.

'Mama showered gifts from Latvia on everyone. Nana got a fine shawl and a wool jacket. Baba had a fancy shirt, Uncle Telman some expensive sportswear and Uncle Salman a fashionable patterned pullover. Mama has so much to say about Latvia and the way people live there, that neighbours and relatives keep dropping in to hear. Nana has had to cook all the time, twice the amount of food, she says. There are no leftovers when as many as ten people turn up at mealtimes to listen to Mama's tales. It sounds like another world.'

'I don't suppose your Nana likes that,' Kima Shamirovna observed.

'I expect so, but the chocolates and flowers they all bring make up for it. Some seemed disappointed that they didn't get presents from Latvia in return.'

I finished chewing on my *pirozhki* and Kima Shamirovna pushed the plate towards me, encouraging me to take another one. Baba's car horn beeped outside. Kima Shamirovna rose, smoothing the crumbs from her fashionable denim skirt and ushered me to the door.

★★★

The novelty of Mama's arrival home with her husband and baby boy did not last long. A few days later, I was sitting at the dining room table, pretending to do homework, but actually doodling, whilst Mama and Jalil chatted in the armchairs opposite each other. They looked as relaxed as a couple in one of the American movies AzTV showed late on Saturday nights.

When Nana walked into the living room, the atmosphere changed. I just managed to hide my artistry under a textbook and take up my fountain pen in time. Though my fingers were stained with ink, from a clumsy refilling, I stayed put, as Nana strode to the singing TV and switched it off.

She sat down on the sofa, arms folded, and frowned. Then sprang up, as if about to head for the kitchen. Head down in my book, I could feel her anger. Obviously so could Mama, who tried to intercept her, as Jalil lit a cigarette. That seemed to ignite Nana who raised her hands and swivelled to address her.

'Maryam, I am not your mule! I cook. I clean. I look after your baby. I make money. You can't just sit on my neck for the rest of your life.'

'What do you want me to do?' Mama said, edging Nana away from the armchairs as if trying to shield Jalil.

'How should I know? Do something, anything! Neither of you has a job. How long will I be buying his cigarettes?' Nana flamed. She stuck her head out like a hungry chicken in Jalil's direction.

Mama was about to reply but pressed her lips shut as Baba walked in. Limping slightly, Baba passed next to Nana, who continued glaring at her daughter, and plonked himself in Mama's armchair.

'You're good with cars, aren't you?' he said to Jalil.

'Yes,' Jalil replied, moving to the edge of his seat.

'Well, the garage I've been building since you went to Latvia will be ready in a week or two. Why don't you start repairing cars there and making some money for your family? Once you've got some customers you could pay me a small rent, to reimburse me for all the trouble I've taken with it.'

'Sure,' Jalil said, beaming.

Baba had grown wiser with age. Everyone relaxed as he put his foot up on a stool and motioned me to switch the TV back on. He had stepped on a rusted nail a few weeks before, which had punctured a hole through his shoe into his toe. The gangrene had started quickly because of his diabetes. Doctors warned that if it spread his whole leg might need to be amputated. For now, they had decided to remove his big toe, with the hope of stopping the gangrene in its tracks. The urgent surgery was due any day. My grandparents were hoping to find a good surgeon, which was a rarity. State run healthcare was appalling because most doctors paid for their diplomas and Baba said he'd rather ask a butcher to chop his toe off than let a bad doctor experiment on him.

'And another thing,' Baba said as the TV announcer droned on in the background, 'I think perhaps you'd both be happier living away from here.'

I looked up from my textbook, trying to suppress my alarm.

'There are two rooms in the semi-basement that you could renovate while you're waiting for customers. You can use one as a living room and one as a bedroom. We usually

rent them out, but I'd rather we have peace in this house.'
He looked pointedly at Nana, while she turned away and
stomped into the kitchen.

I turned quietly back to my sums. Inside my heart sang,
only one floor apart, only one floor apart!

★★★

It took Jalil a couple of days to prepare their rooms. He
was, after all, a skilled decorator. He transformed the two
rooms from bleak, echoing spaces into a comfortable and
cosy home.

Jalil's work in the garage had unexpected perks for me,
too. Within the week, he had installed a reel-to-reel tape-
player in the corner of the garage, which he taught me how
to operate. When he was out, buying parts for the cars, he
let me sneak into the garage, to sit in the shadows, listening
to Queen's greatest hits. The garage reeked with the smell
of oil and petrol, but I loved it there. I would stomp and clap
along to *We Will Rock You*, though my personal favourite was
I Want to Break Free. The advantage of listening on the reel-
to-reel player was that I escaped the frowns and disparaging
remarks from the adults in response to Queen's outfits on
the TV. Each time the Russian television played one of
their songs, someone in the family changed the channel
back to the Azerbaijani station.

The only other singer who caused a similar level of
controversy was Demis Roussos. Every time he belted out
Forever and Ever, in his mesmerising voice, Nana would
push her chair in front of the screen to drink in his image,
her gaze uninterrupted, her eyes wide with wonder, her

lips parted. 'His voice touches my soul,' she said again and again. Invariably Baba would switch the TV off, his jealousy palpable. The only reason Nana was still alive was because she could never meet Demis in person.

★★★

Once Mama, Jalil and almost nine-month-old Khalid had settled, life was a lot better for everyone, including me. Mama and Nana stopped fighting as much. I could escape to see Mama and cuddle up with her, if she had time, without fearing that Nana may get resentful. When Jalil started working in the garage, he earned enough money to support Mama. My dream of the four of us living together rekindled itself. Perhaps it would happen one day after all.

However, within several weeks of their return, Mama's relationship with Jalil began to change. She seemed to have become as frustrated with him as Nana. She said things in front of me: 'You used to change Khalid's nappies in Latvia. And help me wash clothes,' she said, struggling to stir porridge with her right hand while balancing my brother on her left hip.

'We are not in Latvia anymore,' he replied through his nicotine-stained teeth and walked out, leaving me to comfort Mama.

My view, which I kept quiet, was that Jalil was aping my Uncle Telman's attitude, who had never, ever lifted a finger to help Sevil with household chores. It did not fit with his sense of manliness. Instead, he spent most of his time weightlifting in the garden, sculpting his muscular body and expecting to be served his food. Meanwhile, Sevil had to work, raise their two children, clean the house, wash up, and even aid Nana. Jalil seemed to be slowly morphing into my uncle, which made my visits to Mama increasingly uncomfortable.

***

As circles of smoke floated up from Uncle Salman's O-shaped lips, I giggled with delight. We were standing on the street, in front of our sky-blue gates. They were badly chipped in places, mostly from the stones that visitors used to knock on the gates because the bell often was not working. Ordinarily, I was not allowed to play on the street because Nana said *riji*, a wild ginger dog, might snatch me away. I was safe with Uncle Salman, though. He seemed to be in a good mood that day, allowing me to follow him out into the deserted street. The early afternoon sun was beating down on the dusty road that was littered with random stones. The air was filled with the aroma of climbing, pink roses that hung over the gates and covered the adjacent walls.

Uncle Salman inhaled deeply on his cigarette, but instead of popping out more smoke rings, he started to choke and cough. With smoke streaming from his nostrils, he shoved his hand, still holding the cigarette, into the pocket of his grey trousers. I was just about to warn him, when Baba's car pulled up. I tried to think of an explanation for why I was outside. I felt like a taut violin inside but tried to distract him with my smile.

'Hello, Baba, I heard your car!' I chimed, ready to slip quickly back into the house.

His watery, blue eyes, with dark circles beneath, remained stern. He did not look in the mood for greeting anyone, as usual after his twenty-four-hour shift at work.

As he hobbled towards the gates, still pained by his amputated toe, he looked straight past me and barked: 'Why are you on fire, Salman?'

Then he slowly mounted the steps and went into the house, without another word.

A small burning circle was rapidly expanding in my uncle's pocket. As soon as Baba was out of sight, Uncle Salman erupted into curses as he jettisoned the cigarette. Slapping his trousers with his hand, he half ran, half skipped into the back garden. I heard the outside tap thudding into action and caught the scent of singed hair on the breeze. It smelt like when Nana scorched chicken skins after plucking the feathers off. I smiled as I carefully stubbed the butt out with my heel and threw it into the bushes. It was the closest Uncle Salman had ever got to dancing, I thought, as I stepped lightly into the hallway, shutting the door behind me.

Inside, the monotonous tuck-tuck-tuck-tuck sound of Nana's sewing machine explained why she had not heard the drama. She still used the money she made from dressmaking to buy expensive clothes for her children. Though she told Baba they cost much less than they did, he would still complain about her 'spoiling' them.

Baba must have gone straight to bed. He normally slept for half a day after his shifts and allowed no one to watch television while he rested.

I was just wondering what to do next when Uncle Salman slunk down the stairs, like Baghera, the black panther in my favourite Soviet cartoon, *Mowgli*. He had changed into his navy tracksuit and obviously hidden the trousers somewhere he thought Nana would never find them.

He was gulping down a large glass of fruit compote drink. Nana made them all the time, with whatever fruit was in season. Reaching the bottom of the stairs, he thrust the empty glass into my hand, wiped his plump lips and pointed to the kitchen, a soundless order to me to get him more.

As he vanished upstairs again, Nana was suddenly at my side, hands on hips. She stared accusingly at me.

'What have you done now, Gulush? Did you drink all of it?' she said, snatching the glass from me.

'No. It was Uncle Salman, honestly.' He must have seen her coming.

'Hmph,' she exclaimed. 'Well, at least you didn't drink it. I can't believe the cheek of it. A person can't even look away for a second in this household. I thought he was out. When did he manage to sneak in? No doubt that stench is something to do with him. Boys are always boys, even when they're men!' she muttered, pacing into the kitchen.

Mama's soft footsteps approached from behind me and she ruffled my short hair before also making a beeline for the kitchen. I nearly followed her but paused because of Nana's strange behaviour. Instead, I sat in the nearest armchair and pretended to read a book, whilst straining to hear what was being said in the kitchen.

'Is it ready, Mum?' she said.

'No. Your brother drank it.'

A long pause followed, then to my utter amazement,

they both cackled. Nana's laugh was bitter, Mama's was amused.

'What? What's going to happen now?'

'Nothing. It wasn't intended for him, so it won't do him any harm. It's just annoying that I'm going to have to pay again to get it done.'

'Maybe it's a sign. Maybe we don't need to do anything.'

'But I'm tired of your bickering. I won't survive another divorce.' Nana sounded tired now. 'I want you to be happy. Whatever it takes.'

I sat statue-still as Nana returned to mine and Mama's old bedroom, which now doubled as her workroom and Uncle Salman's bedroom. As soon as she was out of sight, I sprinted to the kitchen where Mama was refilling the glass with bright red compote drink.

'Mama, what's happened?'

'Nothing. Just some misunderstanding.' She waved me off, heading downstairs to her room. 'I need to take this to Jalil. It's his favourite.'

'Tell me.' I blocked her way.

She stopped thoughtfully, then shrugged her shoulders. 'Okay. Nana went to a seer and bought a potion. It was supposed to stop our fights, sweeten Jalil's temper.'

I was shocked that Nana had resorted to doing this, even though I had overheard many women telling Nana that they had resolved relationship problems by visiting seers. Neighbours, relatives and even clients extolled the virtues of the dark arts. Why create an open confrontation, if you can seal someone's mouth with an incantation, spell or potion?

Judging by the way Mama's relationship with Jalil was

continuing to deteriorate, I wondered whether Nana had given up on paying for any more potions.

★★★

In the quiet of the house, my violin was singing like never before. I wished someone was home to hear me. Mama, of course, 'I'll show it off to Mama.' I put my violin in its case and went to the semi-basement.

'Aaahhh!' Mama's sudden scream nearly made me drop my violin case. Leaving it on the ground, I ran through the semi-dark corridor that led to their rooms. Had she fallen, or burnt herself cooking, or was there something wrong with my brother?

Although Nana had always taught me to knock before entering any room, Mama was crying, so I flung the door open, just in time to see Jalil, his fist clenched hitting Mama's head.

I flinched, then screamed as if he had hit me and flung myself on Mama. She was curled up into a tight ball on the floor, with her back against the cupboard full of expensive dishes, which Nana had given to them as her dowry. She covered her face, but the rest of her body was vulnerable to Jalil's fist.

Despite my efforts to shield her with my body, Mama pushed me off herself.

'Move away. Let him hit me. Let him feel like he's a real man!'

'Shut up!' Jalil snarled. 'Won't you bite your tongue? Haven't you had enough?' Again, he raised his fist.

I screamed. Now I was scared that I would come to feel that fist as well.

'What's happening? Gulush, why are you screaming?' came from outside the door. I felt as if a heavy weight had dropped off my heart when I heard Sevil's voice.

'Go out there,' said Mama in my ear. 'Don't let her come in. I don't want her to see me like this.' I hesitated. What if Jalil hit her again?

'Don't worry about me. He won't hurt me anymore,' she said, pushing me away.

Reluctantly, I headed for the door, turning to glare at Jalil once I was a safe distance from him, with a look of broken trust. I used to think he was a good man. Why had he changed so much since they moved into our house?

'What's happened?' Sevil demanded, as I stepped through the door.

'It was nothing,' I said, trying desperately to do as I had been told and lead her away. She refused to give up so easily. Unable to hold my tears back anymore, I told her what I had witnessed. I was trembling all over and felt sick now.

'You should have stayed out of it,' she said. Her face had suddenly hardened. 'It is between a husband and his wife. No one should meddle in such things.' She gripped my arms when she said this, then turned away and hurried back to the bungalow at the bottom of the garden where she lived.

My own auntie was telling me to just go home and pretend nothing had happened. How could I do that? Maybe she was relieved that she was not the only one now? Mama was tasting the same flavour of discipline that Uncle Telman had been inflicting on her for years. Even though the couple lived apart physically, there was no real separation from the main household and its edicts: for it was Nana who complained about Sevil to my uncle. I had heard her myself.

'What sort of daughter-in-law is she?' Nana would say, whenever Uncle Telman joined us for a meal. Sevil's list of crimes was endless according to Nana. 'I had to clean in front of your bungalow this morning. It was eight in the morning and she was still in bed. How many times do I have to ask that she turns the water pump on in the morning and waters the trees and vegetables in the garden? Do I have to do it all by myself? She won't call me "mama". Others' daughters-in-law wash their mother-in-laws' feet and drink the water,' she sighed. 'But mine… oh, she's as cold as a fish. Rosa *Khala*, Rosa *Khala*,' she mimicked, sarcastically. 'You have to teach her that whatever is discussed in this household stays in this household. Okay, her parents live five minutes away from us but that's not a good reason to run to them every time something bothers her.'

Sometimes I almost hated Nana for igniting their fights but knew that her own experience had been much the same. Baba had beaten her when they were younger. She told stories about their fights. Again, this was no surprise, older relatives said, because he had seen his own father do the same. It was almost viewed as a tradition.

The aftermath of Nana's discussions with Uncle Telman was usually the same. Sevil would hide away for a day or two and called in sick at work. At home, she applied a layer of dark, gooey *Bodyaga* to her face to help the bruises go away quickly. There was always some in the house. Its strong smell would make my nose tingle.

'It's made of ground sponge, with horse chestnut and arnica. Very potent,' Sevil had explained in her pharmacist voice, as she coated half her face in it.

I wondered whether Mama needed some now. As I tried to make sense of the situation between Mama and Jalil, I went to fetch my violin and take it into the house. The rest of the family were settled round the TV, which was blaring out popular songs. I knew what Sevil had said was what most people thought in our neighbourhood, but I felt I had to check on Mama. By the time I got there a soft silence had fallen. Mama emerged as I approached the door.

She was carrying a plate of succulent black grapes and juicy pears. My mouth instantly watered. Fruit was expensive. There had been little of it in our house recently because most of the money was being used for Baba's medical supplies. Since the gangrene, his health was deteriorating fast.

'Take a piece of fruit,' Mama said.

I could immediately hear Nana's voice inside my head: 'Don't accept food from anyone, even your mum. People barely make ends meet and you cannot assume that they have enough to share.'

Mama urged me with her eyes, the bruises already forming on her face. I did not want to upset her, so I reached out my hand. Jalil's voice hit the air like a whip.

'I bought that for *my* family, not her!' He was standing right behind me.

Jalil had never treated me like a daughter, but this was the first time he had said something like that.

'Don't listen to him, take some fruit,' Mama repeated,

almost pleadingly. She followed me to the main house door, but I did not look back. I did not care if she felt guilty. I wanted to get away, disappear, run until my pain ran out.

9.

SUGAR LUMPS

Kirovabad, Azerbaijan S.S.R., 1987

I had to get over my upset with Jalil quickly if I wanted to see Mama, though I tried to visit her when he was out. On rare occasions that I ran into him, he said hello with reserved distance.

The start of the new school year on 1st of September felt like a relief. I could escape my household and spend time with friends. On the first day, I went to school in a starched white shirt, its collar adorned with a scarlet pioneer scarf, and long navy skirt that Nana made for me. It was the worst length possible – way below my knees but not quite ankle length. I carried a bouquet of roses Nana collected from our and Amaliya *Khala*'s gardens. Compared to my classmates' slick shop-bought flowers, mine looked distinctly shabby. I handed it over to the class teacher and disappeared into the busy corridor to attend my first class at 8am.

After the lunch break, I left the school toilets hastily. Over the three-month summer holidays, I had forgotten that I tried to avoid using them if I could. The flushes were all broken again, the temporary water barrel long since dry – so nothing had been flushed away. The collective smells of the day stewed in the heat to nauseating proportions. Even after thoroughly washing my hands, the smell clung to my clothes and nostrils. I was just taking some refreshing breaths outside when my classmate Samira came panting up to me, like an excited puppy after a ball.

'Gulya! Come to my birthday party. It's next Monday, after school!'

Blue-eyed with blonde locks, Samira looked like an angel. A single child, she seemed to have everything I desired: adoring parents, a big house, beautiful clothes and a legion of admirers. At breaktimes she could buy herself whatever treat she wanted – money was never an issue. She could even choose when to come to classes. If there was a test or presentation that she did not want to do, she was able to skip school because her parents bribed the teachers to close their eyes to her absences. I had always wanted to see her life from the inside. I was surprised at the invitation, but before I could reply, the school bell rang, summoning us back to class. She took my hand, and we ran back together to our Azerbaijani language class. I wished I had taken greater care drying my hands.

Azerbaijani language was by far my least favourite subject. Although I spoke it at home from a very young age, I sensed that it was less valuable to me than Russian. Still, I looked forward to our classes because of the teacher, Natavan Azimovna. She only taught a little grammar and syntax. Instead, she preferred to indulge in long monologues, most of which had nothing to do with the Azerbaijani language. My teacher's stories about Azerbaijan's history fascinated me, especially because these facts were never mentioned in the school textbooks. I had no idea how she knew them, but she seemed to have had interesting life experiences, which seeped into her conversations. She clearly disagreed with the state's communism and I worried she might end up in trouble for this attitude and sharing it with her pupils. She once told us how a member of her family ended up in trouble for possessing a dollar note. She said they were treated like traitors, while her tone betrayed disapproval of the regime.

I sat down in my usual front row seat and watched Natavan Azimovna biting the end of her pen while she contemplated what to share with us.

'They can say whatever they like, but the Azerbaijani Democratic Republic was very progressive for its time,' she said eventually, passion emanating from her through a cloud of black tight-curled hair. 'They let women vote before anyone ever considered such a possibility in the West. And that was in 1918! Imagine what our lives could be today if they had not been squashed by the Soviets in 1920.' She shook her head and clicked her tongue.

Maybe it was because I was in the front row, but she looked straight into my eyes and said: 'I think it's important to learn to think for yourself. Don't just buy all this ideology.' Then she opened the class register.

I sagged, remembering that we were about to read a long poem about a mother who froze with her baby in her arms, in a heroic act of refusal to submit to the Germans during World War II. However, as she opened the book, Natavan Azimovna added: 'Take this propaganda about religion. Didn't work, did it? I bet your grandparents talk about Allah at home, despite all those slogans by Marx and Lenin about religion being the opiate of the masses.'

This remark deeply disturbed me. For years I had

been unable to decide whether I should believe Nana, that Allah would punish me for misbehaving, or school, which advocated the view that there was no such thing as a god. I sat up, hoping she would say more, but instead she called on Tarana to read the poem and the moment passed, leaving the questions I would never dare to ask unanswered.

★★★

'Nana,' I said, that evening. By her expression, though tired, she seemed in a good mood. She was humming as she sat in the back porch chopping a hefty juicy watermelon on a large tray. The red flesh of the watermelon on a hot evening lured me with the promise of coolness. The summer heat had not died back yet.

'Yes, the light of my eyes.'

'Nana, Samira invited me to her birthday party next week. Please, can I go? Please? All the girls in my class are going. Please.' I framed my sweetest, good granddaughter expression with my hands.

'We can't afford an expensive present worthy of Samira's family. Tell her you can't come,' Nana said. Her voice fired that bullet, then she carried on humming.

My disappointment threatened to spill out with my tears. I could not even enjoy the juicy watermelon anymore and made an excuse that there was a TV programme that I wanted to watch. As I retreated into the house, my mind searched for a solution, while my imagination conjured up the interior of Samira's house, the food they might serve and the music they might play. The images were so vivid, I felt I could not give up on the possibility of going.

★★★

On Friday afternoon, I changed from my school uniform into my home dress and was carefully trying to lift the heavy white blanket, which hung over the bedroom mirror. When we were in mourning, Nana always covered up all mirrors to honour the dead. I was not quick enough to replace the blanket when Nana's heavy footsteps came from behind me.

'Gulush, don't look in the mirror during Ashura! You can admire yourself when we are back from Imamzadah.'

Travelling to the largest cemetery in the area was not exactly a social occasion, but I might bump into someone from school. What if my hair was sticking out? Reluctantly, I went to the kitchen sink, wet my hands, and combed my thick short hair with my fingers, as best I could.

'And bring that little bag with sugar lumps,' she said, putting her shoes on.

I wondered what she wanted it for, as I scurried to catch up with her, before she yelled at me again. It was over an hour in an overcrowded bus to get to the cemetery.

Walking to the bus stop seemed more tiring than usual since I had to look mournful because of Ashura. Nana told me that Ashura was a solemn day of mourning Prophet Muhammad's grandson Hussein's martyrdom. When I pressed her for more information, she got irritated and mumbled something about never knowing who was listening. She clearly did not want to advertise our destination.

A rusty, orange bus drew up. Nana and I elbowed our way into the middle of the bus where someone offered her a seat. I was left sandwiched between strangers, clinging to a handrail. The smell of stale sweat was overpowering, no matter what position I chose.

It was a relief when we got off and walked the rest of the way in silence. Soon the dusty air became saturated with a strange sound. It sounded a bit like a bullet whistling, but no guns were fired. Nana remained calm and silent. A steady chant from thick, male voices accompanied the noise: 'Shakhsey-vakhsey, Shakhsey-vakhsey, Shakhsey-vakhsey.' A few moments later, we entered the large graveyard and I saw several men with bare torsos. Mesmerised, my eyes were drawn to their hairy chests, but I looked away before Nana noticed me staring. The men were of different ages. All of them had a stick with an iron chain attached; this was the bullet-like sound. They were swinging the chains over their shoulders where the metal struck bare, bloody and reddened flesh. I had heard Baba talking about this practice. Only men could repent in front of Allah in this way.

'Shakhsey-vakhsey,' chanted the men in unison, as the swinging chains pounded their backs. Next, we walked through the courtyard, shaded by large oak trees, towards what looked like a small one-room temple. A large crowd was gathered nearby. I watched people taking their shoes off and queueing to enter. By the entrance, there was a pile of scarves. Every young woman who approached the door took one and covered her head. Older women, like Nana, had their head covered all the time. I took off my sandals and picked a dark navy scarf, before entering the temple.

Inside, there was a tomb with inscriptions, which I could not decipher. A man sat in the corner and supervised the people who circled the tomb uttering fervent prayers. I followed Nana and, like her, circled it three times. Women in front of us cried in passionate prayer. Some of them crawled or kneeled, kissing the sides of the tomb and looking up, as if to check that Allah had heard them.

I tried to imagine what my schoolteachers might say about this strange ritual. My maths teacher seemed to be a real Communist. I suspected she would disapprove of any superstition but was sure Natavan Azimovna thought differently. Nana always said it was best to weigh your words before talking about religion. Why did my teacher not worry about the children telling their parents about what she had said? As I watched the mournful faces around me, I tried to make sense of her recent comment.

Except for Great Uncle Hussein, no one in my family prayed, not formally, at least. If you wanted to convince someone of your honesty, you swore by Allah's name. Sometimes, they would negotiate with him: 'Dear Allah, if you cure Baba or Nana… help with Uncle's education… help with Mama's job… then we will sacrifice a lamb to you, to show our gratitude.' Nana always asked Allah to punish anyone who had offended her and sometimes he seemed to co-operate, but mostly he was used as a threat. As a child I had no doubt that He was male, stern, frightening and unforgiving. I did not think He loved me, or anyone else for that matter.

Looking at the women whispering ardent prayers, I wondered whether I was wrong to think like that. People looked different when they prayed. When Great Uncle Hussein visited, I had once crept to the door of the drawing room and watched him pray. He was facing away from the door, towards Mecca, so without his hearing aid on he was unlikely to notice I was there. He knelt on a piece of fine black cloth with his prayer beads, a prayer book at his side. As he quickly and quietly recited the words at intervals, he bent to touch his forehead onto the cloth. When he had finished and turned to pick up his hearing aid, he caught me looking, but instead of shouting he smiled gently and put a finger to his lips, his face relaxed and peaceful, then gestured me to go away. He did not tell anyone what had happened.

Before we left the temple, Nana swivelled me around so that we could back out like everyone else. As I took my scarf off outside, I asked her why.

'It's disrespectful to turn your back on such a person.'

'Who is he?' I whispered.

She mumbled something under her breath before answering my question.

'He is the son of Muhammad al Baqir.' My face told her that this did not mean anything to me, so she elaborated.

'He is one of the most sacred personalities of Shiite Islam. This grave has been here for centuries. Twelve centuries, to be precise.'

Then she recited a passage from the Koran, which I had heard from Great Uncle Hussein in the past. Probably to apologise to the dead person for my ignorance. Her mention of Shiahs stirred up some unanswered questions for me. Was I a Shiah too? Why did Nana say I was stubborn like a Sunni, just like my dad, when she was angry with me? The contempt in her voice when she said that had always stopped me from asking what she meant. Were people born into a religion, or could they choose? These questions rolled round in my head, unsaid.

Escaping from the stale air of the semi-dark tomb helped to clear my mind and my questions faded away in the bright sunlight. Nana pulled me towards the back wall of the temple, which was plastered with sugar lumps.

'Make a wish and see whether the sugar sticks to the wall. If it does, your wish will come true,' she said.

I thought it was ironic that we were sticking sugar lumps, part of the monthly Soviet ration (collected alongside some ghastly margarine and thin slices of beef with bone), to a temple wall.

Pressing a sugar lump to the damp wall, I wished first to live with Mama, then to have a present to give Samira so I could go to the party. I added a few more after that. All the lumps stayed put, but I could tell by the ground next to the wall that most fell off in the end. It was littered with half-melted lumps.

'Enough,' said Nana, pulling me away.

We went to the front of the building. Several of the worshippers were handing out halva, a brown mixture made of sugar, plain flour and butter. It was wrapped in thin flat bread and made a great treat. They also served tea to passers-by under the shade of a large oak tree. We each had a small, pear-shaped glass of the strong dark liquid. Standing with other women of all ages, sipping tea, I was momentarily grateful for this warm act of generosity, but then remembered the possible consequences. Nana herself had once said: 'Stepping through the door of a mosque or Imamzadah can ruin a promising career. Islam and Communism do not mix.'

Biting into the wrap of sweet halva pushed these worries down again. I reminded myself that I was here because of Nana anyway, whether the rituals made sense to me or not.

★★★

On the day of Samira's party, I still had no present for her, but I had devised a way of attending.

I told Nana that I would be late home from school that day because I was needed to work on a school poster. Such projects often happened, so she was not suspicious. I was thankful she had forgotten all about Samira. I hoped I could come up with some creative solution for the lack of present, but as the clock ticked round I could not. I was sad to think the other girls were all going to have a great time. When school ended, I walked along with them, subdued by thought. Perhaps I could just say hello and then make an excuse and go home. I might get a view of inside from the porch. The other girls were laughing and chatting. Sparkly bags, no doubt full of expensive presents, swung from their wrists.

Outside Samira's house, I took a deep breath and prepared to say my goodbyes, but it was all so beautiful. The big house, and its tall, bright yellow front door, mesmerised me. I was about to leave when Samira's mother flung the door open and welcomed everyone in.

She looked like a princess. She was wearing a black dress, which fitted her shapely figure perfectly. Her black hair was straightened, with a sheen like silk. Her caramel eyes radiated warmth, and her lips were curved in a soft crescent. Sparkling in the sun, a pair of diamond earrings looked too heavy for her small ears.

I lingered at the back while all the other girls filed in. I kept hesitating, stepping from one foot to another. Now was the time. I had to leave. My excuse would be? Nana was waiting for me? We were invited to a wedding? Samira's mum said: 'Come in, Gulya, come in!'

Without knowing how, my feet had walked me through the yellow door. The voice in my head was telling me to stop, but I kept putting one foot in front of the other, as if sleepwalking. Once inside, everything came into sharp focus. A long square table was laden with freshly chopped tomatoes and cucumbers, rings of fish and salami, feta cheese and flat bread. It was not too late to leave, I reminded myself as I salivated.

I quietly watched the girls pile their presents on a table in Samira's bedroom. Bag after bag, the gifts formed a rainbow mountain in a room where everything felt soft like a cloud, from the fluffed-up pillows and duvet, a delicate sea-shell pink, to fine patterned wallpaper the colour of apricot blossoms. I slipped out of the bedroom shortly before the others, praying no one noticed anything unusual.

Once we were seated at the large dining room table, the feast began. Samira's mum brought plate after plate of delectable foods, some of which I had rarely tasted. My eyes watered at the sight of it all. There were vine leaves stuffed with minced lamb, round dishes of pilau with caramelised onions, chestnuts and big chunks of lamb, an oven-baked golden fish and a whole roasted chicken. Unlike my household, where Nana ranted if I wanted an extra portion, Samira's family seemed genuinely happy when I accepted second helpings. I was full quickly, but I craved more and ate everything the hosts offered.

Once I could not squeeze in any more food, Samira invited us to another room. It was semi-dark until she pressed a button on a video cassette player and *Tom and Jerry* burst onto a big screen in front of us. While the cartoon characters were pummelling each other, we sat in deep armchairs and on sofas, giggling at Tom's misfortunes.

After a while, Samira offered us a tour of the house, but, although curious, I decided to stay put. When else could I watch *Tom and Jerry*? It was never shown on TV and we did not have a video player. Captivated, I sat back in a comfortable armchair in a complete stupor and savoured every minute.

It was only when I heard other girls singing Happy Birthday that, reluctantly, I headed out. The sharp light made me squint, and when my eyes adjusted, I saw a three-layered chocolate cake decorated with candles and colourful berries. I watched Samira blow twelve candles out and joined the girls in a round of applause. As Samira's mum cut the cake, I eagerly waited for a piece to be passed to me. It tasted even better than it looked. Though full already, I forced it down with the help of hot black tea. We thanked Samira and her family, said our goodbyes and set off to our respective homes. I felt like I carried a memory of paradise in my head, as well as my belly. I tried to focus on that as I neared home.

***

At home, I was relieved to find Great Uncle Hussein emerging from the drawing room because I knew that meant Nana, busy looking after him, would barely notice if I skipped my dinner.

Great Uncle Hussein sank onto the opposite end of the living room sofa from me, as I made a show of reading a textbook. The medals decorating his solemn suit jingled mournfully. He had been sixteen years old when World War II began, and he was enlisted into the army. By the end of the war, he had committed many heroic acts, which had earnt him his medals. His head was shaved, and he wore a black skull cap on top of his head. I admired how he managed to keep it on no matter what he was doing. Across from him, Baba sat in an armchair, his expression sour. They were silent together, as they often were, for a few minutes, before Uncle Hussein launched into his usual stream of complaints.

'I nearly lost my life for this country during the war, and what do I get? A flat in the middle of the mountains! Have they travelled on those roads? They are so bumpy that I will never develop stones in my kidneys. Not that I want stones in my kidneys. I just want a home in a civilised part of the country. I come from Baku, my ancestors lived and died there, so should I. But what do the government people do? They offer me a place on a remote island. It's a nightmare to get there. Trains are infrequent and buses are slow. I'm an old man. I need comfort in life. I nearly lost my life for this country. There has to be some justice in this world.'

As usual, he went on and on, whilst Baba silently endured the monologue with the expression of a wet guard dog. Responding to him was a bit pointless anyway, unless Uncle Hussein wore his hearing aid.

'Salman,' Baba addressed my younger uncle discreetly, as soon as he entered the room to greet Great Uncle Hussein. 'Can you check whether he's wearing his hearing aid or not?'

When the answer was 'no', Baba launched into a stream of complaints of his own.

'Inconsiderate idiot! I've been working for the past twenty-four hours and he's telling me about his stupid complaints about the government. What else does he want? After all, the government paid dearly for his participation in the war. Didn't they give him one flat already? He wants to get another one from them? In the capital? Fine! What can I do about it? I just want to rest.'

Sitting on the far edge of the sofa, I watched the two of them lost in their own worlds, muttering endless complaints, only briefly interrupted by Nana's appearance with two glasses of strong black tea and a small bowl of cherry jam with whole black cherries. The adults spooned the jam into small saucers, piling cherry stones on a separate plate and washing down its sweet taste with tea. Normally I would be tempted to reach out for a bowl with chocolates, poised on a shiny metallic tray and ignored by adults, which Nana kept for guests and special occasions, but there was no space in my stomach, even for a Russian Mishka.

Nana did not hug, or even shake her brother's hand, but she did make the mistake of asking how he was. I tried not to smile as he repeated, word for word, the same speech he had just delivered to Baba. The wrinkles around Nana's mouth cut deeply into her chin and upper lip as she listened, but when he paused, she asked him how Arpen was, and he started off again, in minute detail, about her.

After an evening spent listening to Great Uncle Hussein, I think everyone was relieved when it was finally bedtime. I carried a folded-in-three mattress, duvet and pillow from Nana's bedroom, placing it on the hard sofa in the living room. Nana turned the lights off and I curled up under the duvet, ignoring its rough cover against my skin.

In the silence of the night, I relived Samira's party, replaying images of the food, the bedroom and the *Tom and Jerry* video, though my worries about not giving her a present soon came to the fore. I even thought of skipping school the next day as I drifted to sleep, lulled by Great Uncle Hussein's rhythmic snores from the drawing room.

I was so nervous about going to school that I spilt milk all over the kitchen table. I kept anticipating an attack from Samira and tried to think up excuses as I mopped up. As it turned out, the school day was uneventful, and so were the days and weeks that followed. I began to relax, convinced I had got away with it.

However, hearing Great Uncle Hussein at his prayers when he visited often pricked my conscience. Surely Allah had seen what I did? If he indeed existed. He had not sent me a present for Samira, even though the sugar lumps all stuck to the temple wall. Perhaps the fact that no one had found out about my escapade was the real present.

10.

MUSIC

Kirovabad, Azerbaijan S.S.R., 1988

My busy schedule at school and with my music lessons served as an effective excuse to avoid Mama and her family for a while, but my imminent music exams drove me downstairs to ask for help with my practice.

Mama was changing my brother's soiled leggings in their living room. I looked away and wrinkled my nose. As she filled a small round tub with warm water to wash Khalid's chubby bottom, she sighed in exasperation at my request.

'Can't you see my hands are full?'

Mama looked worn out with dark circles under her eyes as if she had not slept much lately. Her belly looked suspiciously fat and I wanted to ask her why, but Khalid gurgled something, before plunging his plump arms into the now mustard yellow water, and the moment had passed.

'Help me wash him then,' Mama urged. 'Don't spill the water on the floor, otherwise the paint will chip away.' I grabbed a grey, plastic jug and poured the warm water over Khalid's arms and legs. She wrapped him in a towel and started dressing him quickly.

'Mama, it's such a big exam. I'll let Kima Shamirovna down if I make a mistake. Can't you just listen while I play?'

I used to hate it when Mama made me practice my scales, but for a moment I remembered, longingly, times before Jalil when she had insisted on watching me play. Though it had usually resulted in me being left alone in tears to practice until I could 'play without stumbling and cringing', at least I had had her full attention then. Afterwards she would sometimes tell me off again, for crying. The sticky marks on the violin, of rosin powder and tears, always betrayed me: but I missed the Mama before Latvia.

'You'll be fine. Stop worrying,' she said, before washing her hands and returning to the board where she had been chopping onions before Khalid's cries had commanded her attention.

'Please, will you come?' I said, hopefully.

'Yes, yes, of course. Now let me get on,' she said.

As I left, I saw her push the hair from her face, then look up again to check Khalid was playing safely. She must have looked at me like that when I was little.

I prayed she was right, that I would perform perfectly. I wanted her to be proud of me and sit in the audience with shining eyes, full of love, that said *'this is my daughter'*.

★★★

As though I were in a trance, my right arm glided over the strings of the violin, playing in unison with Kima Shamirovna's instrument. It was as if I were levitating above my body, watching it playing effortlessly. I did not need to look at my notes today; in fact, I felt like the music was playing me and was stunned by the electrifying sound of the melody all around us.

Today was our final practice session, in a square room adjacent to the exam hall. The ceiling was so high it felt as if our music was reaching up to the sky. When we stopped, I stood quietly with my eyes closed, my body and the air around me vibrating with the magic we had conjured. Suddenly, the silence was interrupted by applause. I turned to look. Mark Lazarevich, the music school's director, was standing by the door.

'Bravo!' he said, as his delicate white hands broke the silence with steady claps. 'Breathtaking!'

I looked at Kima Shamirovna, my face and neck blushing. Had he watched our whole performance?

Kima Shamirovna beamed at me, pride in her round, moist eyes.

★★★

The following week, I stood next to her again but this time on the stage of the music school as a sea of curious faces watched us in wonder. To my best knowledge, not a single student had performed with their teacher before.

Nana had made me a special outfit for this performance: a black skirt with matching short-sleeve jacket, which boasted a hand-stitched silver treble clef, and a snow-white shirt. Caught in the glare of the stage lights, I was unable to make out the faces of the parents and teachers in the hall, which comfortably seated around one hundred people. It felt wonderful that all my hard practice had paid off. Once all the difficult passages were completed, I could relax and enjoy the unison of our violins.

When we finished, I closed my eyes in relief. I had done it, without a single mistake. The lights in the main hall came on, as the audience erupted into a standing ovation. My eyes searched for Mama. I had only ever had a standing ovation once before, in my first year at music school. Now, Kima Shamirovna hugged my waistline and kept pressing me against her side as we watched the audience clapping. The applause continued as Mark Lazarevich came up to the stage. He shook Kima Shamirovna's hand and then reached for mine but, in that moment of triumph, I was distracted. I had scanned all the faces in the audience.

Mama was not there.

★★★

'Gulush,' Nana called. I rushed to lean over the bannister. She was holding a pan of hot water. Time to help, I thought, scuttling down the stairs.

'That man, that director, Mark Lazovich? He is here.' She looked at me quizzically.

'Mark Laza-re-vich, Nana. Why?'

'How should I know? Is anything wrong at your music school?'

'No. My exam went really well. Nothing is wrong. I told you I had a standing ovation again.' My disappointment at their absence during my exam still stung the corners of my eyes.

'Good. Then tell Salman his mother wants a fresh

chicken. Your director is having lunch with Baba.' Her face told me not to ask any more.

As I watched the smooth and calculated moves of Uncle Salman catching the unfortunate bird in the back garden, my brain was racing. I could not think why my music school director had come to visit. He had visited only once before, when I was six. My teacher had wanted me to enter a competition, but it was in Nakhchivan, far away near the Armenian border, so Nana had said no. The director had come and persuaded my family to let me go, with his personal assurance of my safety. I had won that competition and was featured in the local paper. Nana had often boasted about it at family gatherings.

Uncle Salman, having caught the fattest hen, turned to Mecca, its feet under his own and quickly severed its head, keeping the knife pressed down to prevent the dying animal from running around. I wondered if the director wanted me to enter another competition. When the hen had stopped bleeding, he gave it to me. I wrapped it in the calico cloth Nana had given me to stop the blood staining my clothes.

Nana was waiting for me by the water basin. A pan of hot water was steaming on a cold January day. She took the hen off me and dunked it in the pan to soften its brown feathers in hot water, then deftly plucked it bare. I followed her to the kitchen where she singed the chicken, jointed it, and set it to boil with peeled potatoes. Then with pursed lips, she silently prepared a salad and cut some bread, as if I were not there.

When she finally cleared her throat to speak, all she said was: 'Go lay the table, Gulush.'

Carrying in a wicker basket of flat breads and the large plate of cucumbers, tomatoes, onions and coriander and putting them on the table, I strained my ears to hear what Baba and the director were talking about. There was no mention of me, only a brief nod of recognition. Since it was not the custom for me to join male guests, I exited promptly to fetch the plates and cutlery.

When Nana served their meal, she brought a bottle of vodka and two small crystal glasses. The director was rumoured to enjoy his vodka more than tea.

Sniffing the air, thick with the smell of boiling chicken, I paced the living room.

'Stop fidgeting and be patient,' Nana said.

As we were finishing our meal, we could hear the mens' voices becoming louder, possibly because of the vodka. Then Baba called for me. Nana came too.

Standing in the middle of the room, I faced the flushed, skinny face of Mark Lazarevich and suppressed the impulse to lean into Nana who stood behind me.

'There's a job in the symphony orchestra. I want you to take it,' he said.

'She's at school!' Nana exclaimed, as my breath shortened.

'Hear me out. Their salary is three hundred rubles per month. It's a great opportunity for her.'

Everyone I knew with a job earned eighty rubles a month. I could not even comprehend the magnitude of earning three hundred rubles a month at the age of thirteen. Three, hundred, rubles, every month! Nana had to make at least six dresses to make that much money. With three hundred rubles a month I would be able to help her out, and maybe live somewhere with Mama. Now that I knew for sure that Mama was going to have another baby soon, the money would be timely for all of the family. My head was spinning with possibilities as I stood motionless, waiting for their verdict. Baba seemed enthusiastic. His pride shone from his watery blue eyes and smiling mouth.

'Music is not a career for a girl. Teaching it is one thing. Working in an orchestra...?' Nana's body radiated heat behind my back.

'They travel abroad. Paris, London – she could see the world.' Mark Lazarevich's arms stretched out to embrace an imaginary globe. 'She's very talented. Please...'

'Yes. And return with a bunch of bastards I would have to raise,' Nana interrupted him. 'Over my dead body.'

'Don't you want the best for her?' Mark Lazarevich's thin body leant forward expectantly.

I thought of looking at Nana but changed my mind.

'Of course, I do.' I felt Nana stiffen. 'But who will marry a girl who has travelled the world alone? She needs a good husband one day, not a well-paid job.'

Unable to hold back my disappointment, I let a tear roll down my face.

'Rosa.' Baba raised his voice to attract Nana's attention. 'Let's sleep on it.'

Nana mentioned Allah and muttered something under her breath, before speaking again.

'I have made my decision. Thank you, Mark Lazarevich. Perhaps some tea?'

The conversation was over.

11.

CURSED

Kirovabad, Azerbaijan S.S.R., 1988

Sitting alone in the classroom, I pressed my hand over my mouth to suppress a sob, as I looked incredulously at the *dvoika*. I had never had an 'unsatisfactory mark' before. At the break bell everyone else had charged out to buy afternoon snacks, but I felt too shaken to eat. I was close to panic thinking how Baba and Nana might react. I examined my planner to see if there was any way to remove the page without anyone noticing, but quickly realised that there was not.

As I replayed the incident in my head, I tensed up again. It seemed so unfair. I was the only girl who had turned up for the sports lesson. None of the absentees had been penalised. To get a *dvoika*, just for not bringing my sports kit to school, was ridiculous. He said it would 'ensure' I would never forget 'the appropriate clothing' again, but I alone knew that he was wrong.

I had not forgotten. My action was deliberate. I hated changing my clothes in front of the other girls in the dressing room. Unlike theirs, my underwear was plain and basic. I felt awkward running around the school yard while my breasts jiggled with every step. I knew boys stared at them and my backside in jogging bottoms. Besides, I was no good at climbing ropes, jumping lengths or anything like that. I had thought it best to make excuses and dodge the class, until now.

I needed five more *pyatorkas*, 'excellents', before the end of term or I wouldn't reach my expected target. At that moment it seemed impossible. If I did not do it, what would the family say? Another tear rolled down my cheek and landed on the *dvoika*. I decided I had to do something. Checking the clock, I saw there were ten minutes of break left. I tucked my school planner under my arm and ran to the sports hall.

Nazim Askerovich, my sports teacher, was still in the hall. He was talking with his colleague and mother-in-law Asya Azimovna. His marriage, into an Armenian Christian family, had caused some gossip. It was an absolute taboo, at that time, for a woman to take an Armenian husband, but a man's decision to do so was tolerated, though not approved of. I did not personally like Asya Azimovna. With her hirsute top lip, sports uniform and fierce, perfectionist attitude, she was just as threatening as any man.

Unfortunately, Nazim Askerovich noticed me hovering at the edge of the sweat-infused hall before I had fully planned what I was going to do. He beckoned me over. I did not want to have this conversation in front of anyone, but it was too late to turn back. Blushing and wrestling back my tears, I slowly approached them.

'What is it, girl?' He scowled.

'I, er, wanted to ask…' I mumbled.

Asya Azimovna stared at me, but to my relief crossed to

the other side of the hall to prepare equipment for her next class.

'What?' His tone cut like a knife and his brown eyes darted around the hall impatiently. The next class would be bursting through the door at any moment.

'None of the other girls attended the class today,' I said quietly.

He creased his forehead. 'So…'

'But no one else received a *dvoika*.'

His cleanly shaved face softened into a smile. 'Well… That could be fixed, right?'

I nodded vigorously.

'Where does your dad work?' he asked. He was so close now I could smell his cologne. I did not know what my dad had to do with it. I wanted to dodge the question, as I did not want him to know the truth – that I knew nothing.

'He's a… He's a dispatcher for a taxi company.' I stood tall as I spoke about Baba's work instead. I was proud of him, so hard-working, always coming home with pockets of change.

'Oh. I see,' he said. I watched a sudden loss of interest pull his face into one of contempt. Then he simply walked away, dismissing me without a word. I just stood stupefied, until the bell broke the spell.

I felt bitter and humiliated. Didn't they teach us that the ordinary worker, 'the proletarian', should be celebrated? Baba worked so hard. Then I remembered what happened at primary school, when Tarana's disappointment was reversed with a carrier bag for the teacher. How much did Nazim Askerovich charge for his leniency towards the other girls?

Most people I knew, like Nana, did not think girls should be doing physical sports anyway, despite the fact that women were strong enough to do hours of arduous housework. However, though Nana might not care about a top grade in PE, she would care, and ask questions about an 'unsatisfactory mark' and a lower average for the term. As I trailed to my next class, I decided there was nothing else I could do. My family would not pay a bribe and if I asked my teacher to change the grade again, I suspected it would make things worse.

***

Not having a father fed not only a sense of shame, but also made me notice that some girls were adored by their families for the people they were. I did not think I was. Samira, for instance, always had the finest clothes and possessions. This may have been because her mother found it difficult to conceive and did not have another child until seven years after Samira's birth. They seemed to almost worship her, as the child Allah had given them first. Samira was not the only one, I observed.

My schoolmate Farida lived halfway between my home and our school. Every morning I would stop by her house and we would do the second part of my journey to school together. That day I noticed how her dad held her coat out for her, then gave her the same amount of pocket money for the day as I got for a week. He was so warm and affectionate to her, whilst her mother fussed over her long ponytail with hairclips and her grandma wished her a good day at school. Nana seldom spoke like that to me anymore. She saved that tone for honoured guests.

Farida's dad was a policeman and, judging by the freshly decorated entrance hall complete with thick woollen carpet, the family was comfortably rich. Our school uniform was intended to conceal any differences in wealth, but the quality of hairclips, shoes, schoolbags and other trimmings often betrayed a child's real social status. Soviet ideology said I should be proud coming from a working-class family, but, as a teenager, when I saw other people's wealth, it filled me with a sense of failure, and intense envy.

As we walked, Farida and I talked about school, everything from the forthcoming school performance to the challenges of geometry. Soon we were squashed together on the bus. I had a seat but Farida was holding a handrail. The May sunshine streamed through the window, making her short-sleeved summer blouse partially transparent. I could not help but stare. Her armpits were bare.

I did not know of anyone else at school who did that, who shaved, but then it was not something anyone ever talked about. Lots of things like that were taboo subjects in many peoples' houses. I assumed her elder sister, who used to go to our school, had helped her. At that time, I wondered why she had done it.

As the weather got warmer, I became increasingly sensitive about the smell of my own armpits. I washed every morning before school but by the time I arrived, they were sweaty again. The odour seemed to stubbornly cling to my underarm hair, and I thought everyone could smell it as keenly as I did. Forced, by the need for more 'excellent' marks, to attend sports classes had made it much worse, I thought. All the running and jumping left my armpits wet and stinking for the rest of the day. There was no showering at my school. Embarrassed, I would try to sit on my own, but inevitably someone was told to take a seat next to me. I would shrink away from them to the far edge of my chair. I wished I could disappear. I thought it was only me who felt like that.

Then one day I hatched a plan. On Saturday afternoon, as soon as Jalil left the garage, I sneaked in. I switched the tape-player on, keeping the volume low. Queen's 'Under Pressure' seemed an apt soundtrack for my planned activity. Then I reached for the razor that Jalil kept on the windowsill. I unbuttoned my shirt and carefully wetted the razor under the shower in the corner Jalil used to clean up after working on a car. The shower, which was connected to the outdoors water cistern, was lukewarm on hot days. I had seen Baba shaving many times, so I imitated the action, carefully scraping at my armpits. Every few strokes, I washed the hairs off the razor. The water running down my skin as I worked gave me goosebumps, but I was concentrating so hard not to nick myself, as I had seen Baba do, that even when my skin started to sting I carried on. I had acquired a level of skill by the time I started on the second armpit, so it took less time. Trembling, I realised I had forgotten to bring my towel, so I had to rebutton my shirt and hope the wetness would dry before anyone noticed. I rinsed the razor and positioned it exactly as I had found it, made sure I'd turned off the shower and the tape machine and crept out, from the relative shade of the garage into the blazing sun. My eyes blinked protectively, but worse than the light was the burning sensation that had started in my armpits. It was like the pain of grazing a knee, but constant, hard to ignore.

My brain screamed for a solution and I hurried to Mama's living room. Mama was cooking while balancing Ayla, my baby sister, in the kitchen.

'Oh good, I'm glad you're here,' she said, passing the baby to me. 'Can you play with her for half an hour? I have to finish cooking the meal.'

I felt I could not tell her what I had done, so I took Ayla to the living room, but leaving her in the cot, I started to explore Mama's cabinet. I managed to sing a song as I desperately searched for something soothing to put on my armpits. I tried Mama's day cream. Its cool silkiness only lasted for a few minutes then the pain was back. It felt steam hot.

As Ayla had started to cry, I picked her up, but holding her made things worse because it meant I had to press my arms into my body. I found some relief when I held her out and swooped her around, as if she were flying. This made her laugh, but my arms soon got tired, so as soon as I could, I made an excuse of having homework to do and escaped upstairs into the coolness of the drawing room.

The rest of the day passed in much discomfort. The hours dragged slowly and painfully. I had to keep making excuses to go to another room and wave my arms around. The burning was beginning to lessen, or maybe I was becoming used to it, but it was still far from comfortable. Then, at last, it was bedtime. When I finally lay in the dark, I stretched my arms above my head, exposing my armpits to the night air. With tears pricking my eyes, I eventually drifted to sleep.

Nana's voice jolted me awake the next day. It was Sunday morning, so I was usually allowed to sleep in for a little longer than on school days. Nana, having thrown the curtains open, was standing in the path of the light, staring at my shaven armpits. Her face was full of rage. Instinctively, I clapped my arms to my sides, but knew it was too late.

'Who told you to do that? Tell me immediately! Was it your mother?' I shook my head in horror. Nana had fights with Mama every other day and I did not want to cause her more trouble.

'Who was it then? Sevil? It must be her. She hates our family, and this is her way of getting back at us.'

I shook my head again.

'You couldn't have thought of this on your own. Someone surely showed you what to do. Tell me who it was now!' She gnashed her teeth. 'How dare you do such a thing without my permission? Today it's your underarms, what is it going to be tomorrow? Your pussy?' I caught her hand before she could pull my night dress up to check on my pubic hair. 'Next thing I know you'll be a whore!'

It hurt me so much when Nana said things like that. Her insults rained down on me, as tears seeped from my eyes. I knew not to respond. Eventually she was lost for words and stormed out of the room. I dressed quickly and painfully, quivering with frustration and anger.

Was even my body not my own? Did I need her permission for everything? There was no way I was going to tell her about Farida. She would ban me from seeing her. I decided that once she had calmed down, I would tell Nana I had seen something about shaving on Russian TV. She would stop me watching it until she forgot about the incident. Pausing for a moment, I admired my smooth, though still slightly swollen, armpits in the mirror. Judging by Nana's reaction, the next time they would be this smooth again would probably be the day when I became a bride.

★★★

Mama was walking quickly. I tried to keep up with her, whilst dodging the stones that littered the road and might damage the front of my shoes. The street was quiet, and the dim lights of the houses were not bright enough to light the pavements. The air was balmy after the scorching sun of the day. Baba was ill, and Nana had sent Mama to collect a blood pressure monitor from a relative. I had to come because Mama was not supposed to be unaccompanied after dark.

'Listen.' Mama's voice sounded croaky, as if the words were catching in her throat. 'I have something important to tell you.'

My head started to sift the possibilities. Was she moving again? Separating from Jalil? Having another baby? So soon?

'I think something is going to happen to you soon. Don't get scared when it does.'

Her words filled me with dread. What was she on about? I felt lightheaded, as if one of my sudden nosebleeds was about to start.

'I don't know exactly when, but you may find some blood in your pants or on your bedclothes. You will have to tell Nana straightaway.'

She stopped to hug me close. 'Don't worry, it happens to all of us.'

'Even to you?'

'Even to me,' she laughed and seemed to relax. Then we walked on, this time arm in arm.

As we headed up the street, a distant memory flashed into my head. Mama on the phone to her friend, then Nana coming in and shouting.

'That's right, you wasting time chatting, whilst I scrub pussy blood off your sheets!' She had waved them at Mama, who had blushed, quickly put the phone down and followed her back into the kitchen where raised voices had been heard. Though mystified I had blushed too. I never liked it when Nana shouted. Despite the warm evening, the memory made me shiver. What if I bled at night? I imagined the scene, Nana shaming me this time.

'Does it happen to Nana too?' I asked.

'Not anymore. It stops eventually. She's having the menopause.'

'Lucky her. I wish I had the meno-thing.' I sighed. I did not understand why Mama laughed then chuckled periodically all the way home.

As I put on my pyjamas that night, I kept thinking that being born female sometimes felt like a curse. There were so many limitations on where I could go and when, who could be my friends, what I could wear or do with my body, and now this... These thoughts made me feel small, trapped and alone.

12.

ABSENCE

Kirovabad, Azerbaijan S.S.R., 1988

Nana sat very still at the oval dining room table, while I threaded her needle. On her lap, she held the thick navy fabric she was transforming into a dress for a client. My homework was now forgotten on the table. Nana was talking about my father. No one else ever mentioned him. Sometimes I wished she did not either.

'He stood over your crib and cursed you as soon as he laid his eyes on you,' Nana said, as she pierced the fabric with her long needle.

Trying to distract myself, I inhaled deeply, breathing in the smell of boiling lamb that wafted from the kitchen.

'But why?'

'Because you were a girl, of course,' she said without looking up.

I stared back at my school notepad. All the Russian letters blurred together. I busied myself erasing an invisible mark on one of the pages. My shoulders drooped while I waited for her to speak again. She cleared her throat and spoke in a softer voice.

'Don't you worry. Allah punished him.' She twisted her lips in concentration as she rethreaded her needle.

'How, Nana?' I asked, trying not to sound too interested.

'He got three more daughters in his second marriage,' she observed.

I attacked the imaginary mark a second time. The paper was getting thin. What could be worse than one daughter? Four daughters. It sounded almost like a joke in my head, except it was not funny. I thought of my baby sister. She was not celebrated much, but at least she had not been cursed. I had overheard that Mama had gone to hospital trying to get something called an 'abortion'. To give the baby away, I thought. This was because they did not have enough money. Jalil had stopped working in the garage. Baba had followed Mama to the clinic and stopped her. I was glad he did that. I liked having a little sister, even though she got more of Mama's attention and I had to help out.

The page I was rubbing ripped as Nana added: 'It was his loss anyway. You were such a remarkable child. When you were born, I picked you up and you looked straight into my eyes. Babies don't normally do that.' A slight smile lingered on her lips. She looked almost dreamy, forgetting all about the fabric in her hands. 'I can't describe it. There was so much wisdom. As if you had known me all your life.'

My stomach relaxed and I began doodling on a blank corner of *Soviet Pravda* that Nana was reading earlier. She had discarded the newspaper within a few minutes, muttering under her breath that it failed to live up to its name – 'Soviet Truth'. Sitting at the dining table with Nana when she was in a good mood was a treat, even if her conversations interrupted my homework.

'What else do you remember, Nana?'

'You were such a tiny baby. You could fit inside my palm.'

I looked doubtfully at the size of Nana's palm. No. Surely, I was never that little.

'I washed you every day. Once, when I was bathing you, our neighbour Amina came. She saw you naked and exclaimed: "Rosa *Khala*, what is that hanging between her legs? I thought this was a girl"!'

'What was it, Nana?'

'You were so skinny that your 'bits' looked rather pronounced.'

I squirmed in my chair. I found some things Nana said more embarrassing as I got older. Her favourite threat was: 'I'll squeeze spinach oil out of your pussy if you misbehave!' I hated it every time she said that.

She seemed to have sensed my discomfort. She set her fabric down, stood up and turned towards her bedroom.

'Come, follow me,' she said. She rummaged in her pocket and produced her wardrobe key.

The chemical smell of Naphthalene hit my nose; it discouraged the moths and me from nosing around on the rare occasions her door was left unlocked. Nana hid money, jewellery and other 'odds and ends' among the stacks of towels and clothes.

'This is the shirt you were wearing when we brought you home from the hospital.'

'I was that tiny?' I held up the white cotton shirt and surveyed it with disbelief.

'And this,' she unwrapped another piece of material, 'was your hair.'

I looked inside the bundle. A handful of light blonde locks sat there.

'I was blonde, Nana?'

'You were then. I don't know who you took after.'

I thought I knew. When I was much younger, I had heard Mama and Nana complaining about Riji. Nana said something called 'alley mony' did not cover even my music school fees. I thought she was talking about a wild ginger dog when she told me not to play out on the street in case Riji snatched me. Now I realised she had meant something quite different. I had always thought my father never wanted me. Perhaps I had been wrong.

I returned with Nana to the dining table, lost in my thoughts. It was a while before I broke the silence.

'What else, Nana?'

'Well, you might have had intelligent eyes, but you were so ugly. Everyone who saw you at the hospital said that.' She paused for dramatic effect. 'Except for Baba. He picked you up and said, "You lot, you just wait! See what a gorgeous girl she will become." And he was right.'

I stared without comprehension at the Russian-language assignment in front of me; I could not absorb a single word. My bladder was full, but I did not want to break the spell of the moment. Squeezing my legs together, I prayed for more stories. I did not have to wait long.

'You were two weeks old when you came here with your mama, to celebrate *Novruz*. Afterwards, Baba refused to let either of you leave.'

Silence, like rolls of fabric, lengthened between us, as I let her words sink in. It was strange that my father's family had let Mama and me spend *Novruz* away from our new home. There was a superstition that if someone did so, they would not return for seven years. The celebration of the spring equinox was the most important festival. Perhaps they did so because of the tradition that required the mother to look after her daughter and granddaughter for several weeks, just like Sevil's mother did when her children were born.

Though I would usually have waited for Nana to say more, my full bladder pressed me to ask: 'Why didn't you let us go back?'

Nana's face contorted. 'Because your father was crazy. His parents, may they rest in peace, were good people, but he was... a taxi driver,' she spat with contempt. Her shoulders were tensed up now, her fingers clutching into fists.

'Then why did she marry him?' I blurted out.

'He kidnapped her.' Nana shot the words out. 'There was nothing we could do about it. Let this be a lesson for you. Once you lose your virginity, you are nothing! A husband is not a dress you can return to a shop. It's for life. Choose wisely.'

I flinched as she barked the words out, like she had memorised them. Since I'd started my periods, all our conversations seemed to lead to this, the importance of virginity.

The dusk was giving way to night, so I turned the lights on for her.

'May Allah light up your eyes.' Her thank you was of a softer tone than before. Still intent on her sewing, she added more to the story.

'I tried to save that marriage, but both your father and my

139

Ali, your grandfather, were very stubborn; two Aries locking horn to horn. Your father said, "She will not work." Baba said, "She will." Your father often got paranoid with jealousy. He wanted to know what your Mama was doing at every minute. He didn't even like her looking out of the window. When she was doing so one day, he came from behind and chopped off one of her braids! I don't think I can ever forgive him for that. I'd spent years looking after her hair. She had beautiful hair then, which hung below her waistline, but though she struggled, he hacked one of her braids right off!' Nana shook her head in disbelief, whilst I wondered whether that was why Mama had kept my hair short.

'When we found out that your father was beating her up,' she continued, 'Baba wanted to bring her back straight away, but I wouldn't let him.'

I was shocked by Nana's words, but I asked the question anyway: 'Why did you let her stay, Nana?'

'You had to be born before she came home, or people might have said you were a bastard.'

I knew Nana and others thought there was nothing worse than that. I had heard parents talk about Tarana's mother on school runs. One had said it was surprising that she had not been executed by her male relatives, for bringing such disgrace on their family.

My thoughts snapped back to our family.

'What happened after I was born then?' I asked.

'I brought you up like my own. I even gave you my breast!'

I was confused.

'There was no milk, of course, but you took it as a comforter quite happily. You were a clever little thing.

140

When you were only three months old, if I said you had been a bad girl, you would cry. How did you know what I meant? Once, when you were six months old, you were crying, and I was watching from a distance. You cried once, then stopped, then cried, then stopped. You were listening for me. When I didn't come closer, you patted your own chest, exclaimed 'a-a-a' then reached for your bottle and drank from it. So clever.'

Where was Mama when all this was going on? I wondered but did not have the chance to ask, because Nana started clearing her things away.

'Look at the time! Your Baba will be home soon, and the dinner isn't ready yet.'

'But Nana…'

'You're doing it again,' she replied guardedly. 'Making yourself upset.' I quickly adjusted my expression, as she turned to stalk into the kitchen.

'I'm just nipping out back,' I shouted as cheerfully as I could, and dashed to the toilet.

I had not understood why Nana got angry when I was upset, until two months before when I had overheard her talking to our neighbour Amaliya in the garden. They were drinking tea in the shade. I was undressing in the bedroom, the window behind the lime curtains was open.

'It's extraordinary, Amaliya,' Nana said. 'She has never even seen that man, yet when she is sad or upset her eyebrows take on the exact shape of her father's. Also, she squints her left eye like he did when it's sunny. It drives me mad! If she does that, what else might she do like him? It's not like we know much about the women in his family. Who knows what she might have inherited!'

'But if she looks like him, that's a good thing, isn't it?' chirped Amaliya. 'They say a girl that looks like her dad will be happy in life, happily married.'

'What nonsense you speak, Amaliya,' Nana had retorted. 'Tarana's mother looks like her father…'.

What Amaliya said had made me smile then. Now, as I made my way at a snail's pace to the kitchen to help Nana, I tried to imagine what my life might have been like if Mama and I had returned to him. Perhaps, like some fathers, he would have changed as I got older and doted on me. When other kids teased me, I would have said, 'I'll tell my dad'! I wished I knew how much like him I looked. My hand was on the kitchen door when I had an idea. Nana was humming again, chopping something.

I tiptoed into the drawing room and flicked on the light switch. The big chandelier, with hanging crystal petals and six small light bulbs, came alive above me. I slowly opened the middle drawer of the heavy sideboard and pulled out several leather and fabric-bound albums, placing them on the square table. Some were so old their gilt decorations had faded, their surfaces were cracked. I did not know why I had not thought of them before. Perhaps because they were full of hundreds of photos depicting people I did not know. Nana and Baba had spent hours trying to label them but had given up after just two volumes and many arguments about who was who.

One picture was all I needed to find. Turning the thick pages of the first album, with its dark navy velvet cover, I took out each photograph. Many had dates and places written on the back of them, some even had names. Nizami Guliyev, I reminded myself. I had seen my birth certificate with his name in black ink, written in large, tidy letters. I turned page after page, convinced that I would recognise him straightaway. After all, no one else in the family had my green-grey eyes. Baba's were watery blue, quite different from mine. Mama's complexion was dark. It might be harder to identify him on the cheaper, black and white pictures, but I was convinced I must look like him.

I had to finish before Nana came looking for me. I flipped more quickly through the large group shots, especially if Baba or Great Uncle Hussein was in them, then decided that reading the backs was a better strategy. I could feel my heart beginning to race as I pored over the names and dates. Sometimes there were short messages. 'Hussein in Dashkasan, 1979', 'Minaya, Uncle Abbas's daughter, 1981', 'From Nizami to Maryam, with love, 1973'. I nearly glossed over that one in my haste.

'From Nizami to Maryam with love'.

I re-read the message, my fingers shaking with excitement. Was this it? I shut my eyes for a moment to calm myself. Then I opened them again and turned the photo over. A young man, in a Red Army uniform, similar to Uncle Salman's, gazed steadily back at me. Even in black and white I thought he looked nothing like me. His eyes were dark, he had a large, rounded nose, mine was straight. His lips were thin, but with a wider mouth, the opposite of me. As I stared into his eyes, it seemed that not only their colour but their expression was dark. I wished I had not looked. Before this I had had my imaginings, some hope. Now I felt I had nothing.

'Gulush, come here. Your dinner is ready!' Nana called

from the kitchen, pulling me out of my stupor. I could not believe how long I had been sitting there. I vaulted from my seat and hurried to tidy the albums away in the order I had found them, after I had hidden my father's photo in my geometry textbook.

Despite my initial disappointment, I became inseparable from the photo, transferring it from my school bag to under my pillow every night. The only photo that was equally revered in the family was what I assumed to be a portrait of the Prophet, which Nana kept wrapped in an embroidered black silk cloth, on top of the drawing room cupboard. It was tradition that it be placed above everyone in the house. Occasionally I would see her kiss it or press it against each of her eyes in turn, as a mark of devotion. I did not tell anyone about Dad's photo, lest they tell Nana, or gossip about my not having a father.

As I grew used to my father's image, I started to see similarities. The shape of our eyebrows was, as Nana had said, the same. Even his eyes were a bit like mine. His jaw was bigger, but he was a man after all. As a girl, I simply had a smaller version of the same shapes. I soon convinced myself that we were alike and that my dream of being happy one day would come true.

★★★

A few weeks later, my geometry seemed like a stubborn nut that I could not crack. I read and re-read the exercise, looked at the notes I had taken in class, but still could not master it. To distract myself, I stared at my dad's photo, wishing he was there to help me. As a taxi driver, he might not be much help, but at least I could have told him how much I was struggling. I imagined him hugging me and saying it did not matter.

If I failed to complete my homework, my teacher would be annoyed. I puzzled what to do. Baba and Nana had not learnt geometry, my uncles were useless and, though Mama was fluent in Russian, she was not in mathematics. That only left one person, Sevil. Without thinking, I bookmarked the exercise and headed downstairs to find her.

A brood of hens in the garden greeted me with loud clucking expecting some seeds as I entered Sevil and Uncle Telman's bungalow.

'Sevil,' I called out. 'Please help. I'm stuck.'

As she set aside the sharp knife she was chopping vegetables with, the smell of raw onions made my eyes water, giving an excuse for the tears of frustration that now flowed, as I threw the offending book on the table.

Sevil wiped her wet hands on her floral apron and picked it up.

'Don't panic. Is it geometry again?' she asked kindly, turning to the bookmarked page. We gasped together: I because I suddenly realised what I had used as a bookmark, Sevil because she'd found the photograph of a strange man.

I tried to grab the book back, but she held it fast.

'Who is this?'

'No one. It's nothing.' I managed to pull the book from her grasp and hold it behind my back.

'You can tell me, Gulush,' she said. 'Come on now.'

I knew I could not, not yet. I needed time.

What if she told Nana? That thought made me feel sick.

I'd tell her Sevil made it up, or that she'd been mistaken, it was a picture for a school project. Sevil was smiling at me, like she could see the thoughts racing faster and faster round my head, stumbling over one another. She was the adult, I the child not to be trusted. As my mind went blank, my legs did the thinking and I found myself running away.

I arrived back at the house to find it deserted and so quiet I could hear every heavy breath as I panted to my bed and threw the covers over me, clothes and all. My mind started to sift through the possibilities once again. A schoolgirl crush that I'd already discarded? Not that, Nana had made such a fuss when a boy had asked me to marry him when we were seven, heaven knows how she'd react to that now. Last time she'd made an official complaint, but this time? Baba had hit Mama when he'd found a photo of her friend's boyfriend. What would they do to me? The only option seemed to be to deny everything. Pushing the now hot sheets off me, I hid the photo in a space I'd found behind the ornamental carvings on the sideboard whilst polishing it one day.

I returned to the drawing room to puzzle over the geometry, when suddenly the door flung open and Mama charged in.

'Gulush, are you dating someone? Don't pretend you don't know what I'm talking about. Sevil's told me everything! I can't believe you chose to confide in her and not me.'

'Shhh, Mama, I'm not dating anyone.' I rushed towards her, practically hissing in her face in case Nana overheard us.

'Then why did you show it to Sevil? Do you want her to start gossiping about you? Who is in the photo?'

'Dad!'

'What? Do you mean *your* dad?' She was suddenly still, rooted to the spot, like a tree in winter.

'Yes, I found it in one of the albums.'

'Impossible! I tore them all up years ago.'

'Well, you missed one. Here!' I pulled the photo from its hiding place.

She took it out of my shaking hand, looked at it and then she smiled.

'You think this is your dad?'

'It says from Nizami to Maryam with love,' I said slowly. Mama was now grinning broadly.

'Of course, he would put that. He's my cousin Nizami. Why didn't you recognise him? Cousin Nizi, in the Red Army.'

I shook my head and slumped onto a nearby chair. My legs felt like the *kissel* we'd drunk at school.

'Don't cry,' Mama said. She reached to touch me on the shoulder. Then she said, 'Listen, if you really want to see him, I could arrange for a meeting.'

I stared open-mouthed at her. Did she really mean it? Her face was serious.

'But I must warn you of one thing. If you decide to see him, it will break your grandparents' hearts. They'll think that you don't love them. After everything they've done to raise you, it'll be a betrayal. But it's your choice. Do you want to see him?'

As I imagined Nana's and Baba's disappointed faces, my stomach churned, because after that I knew there would be anger. Nana would see me as a traitor, and Baba, though he could be so kind, his anger, once roused, was far

147

worse. Besides, he was ill, and I did not want to upset him unnecessarily.

'Tell me what you want to do,' Mama asked. Her eyes gazed at me with glistening intensity. I nearly spoke. I nearly told her everything that I was feeling, but at that moment she looked so small and vulnerable, like she was the child. So, I shook my head and turned away, until she quietly left the room.

Shutting my eyes, I sat there, wrapping my arms onto my hunched shoulders, pulling my legs in protectively, like a hedgehog, and cried. My head ached as I supressed the sound. I had missed my only chance to ever see him. For a short while I did not care how long I would be there, then I heard the sounds of people returning home along the street. My survival instinct kicked in. I straightened up and reached for my schoolbooks. As I did, I felt a ray of hope glimmer in my heart. I must look like my dad after all.

13.

FAREWELL

Kirovabad, Azerbaijan S.S.R., 1989

In early June when my summer school holidays began, Uncle Salman drove Baba, Nana and me to Hajikand, a little village up in the Lesser Caucasus mountain ranges, where we used to have picnics when I was little. The smell of fresh tarragon and flat bread, packed for our mid-morning snack, wafted from the boot of the car.

The windy roads were quiet, and the steady pace of the car lulled me into a daydream. I remembered the times when Baba was healthy, and we had daytrips to these mountains as a whole family. The car used to be packed and inevitably I had to sit on someone's lap. Baba's idea of a picnic was to buy a lamb to slaughter, make kebabs on iron skewers and cook them to perfection on amber charcoals.

While Mama and I had collected flowers and sweet-scented herbs, Nana boiled water in a Russian samovar ready to brew black tea infused with the scent of burnt wood and mountain herbs. Baba and my uncles took care of the food and did the only type of cooking they ever did – kebabs. I could still remember the smell of sizzling meat on glowing charcoals, a treat I had not tasted for a long while because all the resources in the family had been directed at Baba's medication and doctors, since he had developed a persistent cough several months ago. Nana had taken him to many hospitals in Baku, seeking out the best doctors through her network of connections. No matter who they saw the answer was the same, there was little left that any doctor could do to alleviate Baba's discomfort.

When the car stopped, Uncle Salman climbed out of the car and opened Nana's door.

'Go stretch your legs, I'll stay with Dad,' he said.

The birdsong filled the clean mountain air. The green hills, covered in thick forests, and the peak of the magnificent Mount Kapaz disappeared into the morning mist. Hajikand was always cooler than Kirovabad, which was down in the foothills on the Ganjachay river. I zipped up the navy collar of my red jumper, pleased that I wore it over my short-sleeved flower-patterned dress.

The sweet aroma of rosehip blossom pulled me towards the wild hedgerows, which framed the roadside. Seeing the abundance of pink petals, Nana decided to collect two bags to make a delicious fragrant blush-coloured jam at home. The scent of the velveteen pink petals was intoxicating, as I dropped them into a big floral bag Nana had made recently. From time to time, I peaked at Baba sitting in the car, unable to walk around. His expression was bitter, though occasionally his face brightened up as if he remembered something he once enjoyed.

When one of the bags was full of petals, Nana handed me a tarragon and feta cheese wrap. We ate in silence and I returned to the petal picking with my mouth full. The repetitive movements, coupled with the stillness of the morning, had a mesmeric, soothing effect on me.

By the time Uncle Salman started waving me back, I for one did not want to leave. I was left in peace here, unlike at home where there was nowhere to hide from constant demands of the adults. I could even think about my father, or rather his absence in my life. Given how quickly Baba's health had deteriorated, I was glad that I turned down Mama's proposal to meet him.

'Hurry up, your Baba is tired,' Nana said, and her tone whipped me into action.

Back home later that afternoon, the house was filled with a heady mix of strange aromas bubbling from pots in the kitchen as Nana concocted medical potions to comfort her one and only love. While I chopped two large onions, Nana steeped different herbs in four medium pans on the hob. She set them aside to cool and I placed a large cast iron frying pan on the empty hob, added a big dollop of butter and started frying the onions. From the corner of my eye, I watched how Nana carved out the middles of the large, white turnips and filled them with pure honey. She had to wait all day for the honey to drip out of each turnip's taproot into a cup, before making Baba drink the mixture to ease his cough.

I watched Nana preparing this mixture every day and admired her determination to revive Baba. She even contemplated taking him to his birthplace, as someone told her it often helped sick people to reconnect with their roots and draw strength from their ancestors. Unfortunately, Baba was born in Armenia and that country had decided to evict 200,000 Azerbaijanis a few months before Baba fell ill. Our country treated Armenia's actions as a declaration of war and, given that the conflict was escalating, Nana decided that it was not safe to take Baba to his birthplace. She would much rather he died peacefully in his own bed than be manhandled in another country. The truth was that Baba had neither the energy nor the stamina for even the shortest journey. After this setback, Nana threw herself into her remedy making with new vigour.

At first, I was optimistic that Nana would turn the situation around. When I was five, Nana had been discharged from hospital with a kidney dysfunction and was sent home to die. They had told her she only had days to live. That same day, one of our neighbours came to visit and told her about a healer in the spa city called Kislovodsk. This woman was known for miraculous recoveries through her herbal remedies. Baba had somehow convinced Nana to travel to Kislovodsk. Nana could barely stand up at the time. Her body retained all the liquid she consumed and the bags under her eyes were so large that her face looked twice its size. I had no idea how Nana managed a long flight over Georgia to the North Caucasus region of Russia, but after the summer in Kislovodsk, she returned not only healthy but also knowledgeable about every herb under the sun.

Now was different. As Nana picked up steeped herbs from the windowsill and started mixing them with spices, roots and oils to make natural remedies to put some colour back into Baba's pale, worn-out face, and relieve his pain, I turned away. Despite Nana's best efforts, Baba's condition got worse not better. He was now bed-bound. Nana moved Baba's bed to the living room where she could keep an eye on him while making dresses for her clients in the daytime. At nights, Nana, Uncle Salman and I took it in turns to care for him.

The first few nights I hardly slept, each groan and grunt had me getting up to check on him. I worried about what I should do. How would I know if he was worse? How would I know when to call for help? What if he died and I did not notice? His regular, loud snores were a comfort of sorts but as the weather grew hotter, without a blanket to muffle my ears, all I could do was doze until the dawn light started to show through the thick sickly green curtains. Only then did I start to feel relaxed, knowing my shift would soon be over.

On the nights that Nana cared for Baba, I enjoyed having her bed to myself. The couch in the living room made my body ache, so it came as a shock when one day Nana's voice pulled me from my dreams, and I found her standing beside me.

'Still sleeping, Gulush! Some of us have been working hard. Get up and hurry. Go buy Baba some clotted cream for breakfast.'

She repeated the request, the urgency in her voice growing stronger, and I knew it was pointless to argue. My eyes burned under heavy lids, as I slipped off the soft mattress and pulled on my blue floral dress.

'But Nana, I went to bed so late…' I mumbled. There was no point in complaining. Bleary eyed, with just a sip of water, I took her purse from the table and tiptoed to the front door.

A cool breeze caught my face. Mama was by the water basin. Perhaps she would take pity on me and go to the shop for the cream instead? As I drew closer, my weary brain was pricked with sudden jealousy. She was washing Ayla and Khalid's clothes. She was up at this hour for my baby siblings, but not for me, or even her own father.

'Morning,' she said. She sounded as tired as me. 'You're up early.'

Her eyes were puffy. I doubted she had even drunk her morning coffee, fresh, thick, dark and far stronger, Uncle Salman said, than the muck they served in Russia. She would not function without it. I had struggled to wake her when we shared a bedroom to get her to style my hair or sign a note before school. Yet now here she was, up early.

Pursing my lips, I tried to suppress my anger, but it seeped out as sarcasm.

'I didn't want to be up this early. Baba must have fallen from the sky in a basket, because I have to go buy him clotted cream, again. Never mind that I hardly slept last night. He's so important, to us all, obviously.'

My bitterness tasted like rotting teeth. I wanted her to feel my anger, even though I could not aim it directly at her.

'He's ill…' she tried to reply, but I banged the iron gate behind me and trudged down the dusty, silent road to the nearby shop, from which, every weekday morning, some local women sold clotted cream outside before the shop itself opened. I was just in time to buy a jar and hurry back, so that Baba could have cream for his breakfast.

Entering the house, I heard Baba croak through his cough.

'Bucket!'

Leaving the clotted cream on the table, I helped him up on his elbow, to spit into the rusty bucket. His spit was always bloody these days. I had learnt to keep my face calm. I waited, holding him and the bucket steady, watching his skin turn bluish from the tension of coughing so violently.

He was so thin now that his features protruded from his hollow face and he could not get comfortable for long. Even the softest mattress available could not cushion his fragile pelvic bones. Eventually he collapsed, exhausted, back onto the square pillows Nana herself had stuffed with the finest feathers she could pluck from any of our hens.

'Come and talk to me,' Baba said when he finally recovered his voice.

The daily news was starting on Russian TV. It crossed my mind to turn it off, or switch the Russian Channel to AzTV, which Baba preferred, but today he seemed oblivious, so I let the stern-looking commentator, in suit and tie, continue to deliver his latest bulletin of worrying news. This time it was about the cutting of an electric fence between Hungary and Austria. Dragging a wooden chair closer to Baba's bed, I sat with my hands on my lap as if I were at school. I felt I had nothing to talk about. Every story or anecdote I knew I had already shared with him. The silence between us made me squirm inside, but again I gently took his bony hand in mine.

He had always been a man of few words and fewer smiles. Even though he was a shadow of his former self he could still be intimidating at times. I alone had never been beaten by him, but I knew what he was capable of. He might seem helpless now, but my memories were enough to keep me alert every time he spoke, though it was getting increasingly difficult to understand him. Only Nana had the knowledge to translate what he said. Perhaps his voice did not affect her in the same way as the rest of the family.

When I was sure he was asleep, I turned towards the television to see Princess Diana walking with her sons in

London. Gingerly, I placed Baba's shrivelled hand by his side and stared, fascinated, at her image on the screen. Her elegance and charm filled me with longing – I wanted a life like that. Perhaps if I became a diplomat when I grew up, I could live like that too, at least the travelling part. My inner critic immediately started its work, pointing out all the reasons why that would never happen, but before it got on to the bit about my realistic future, as a housewife, I shut it, and the TV off, by going to fetch more tea.

I returned only a kettle's boil later to find Nana by Baba's side. He was holding her hand and speaking rapidly, as if he might run out of time, determined to tell her everything he had on his mind. My heart started to pound; Nana was crying.

'I know I never told you this, Rosa, but I love you. I've loved you all my life. You've been my best friend, my best ally. Thank you for looking after me, thank you for your loyalty.' With a sudden surge of energy, he pulled himself up in the bed. 'There are so many things I've never said to you,' he continued. 'Take this house. Why do you think I spent half of my life building it? Do you remember when we went to visit your old home? You only lived there until your mother died, but I thought you deserved to have a grand house like that again. I worked hard for that to happen for you, because you deserve the best in this life! Can you forgive me?'

Nana nodded as her tears fell faster.

'Can you forgive me, for hitting you?' His voice sounded more urgent now as he searched her face. 'For breaking your ribs with a shovel, just after you had Telman? I didn't know any better then. I saw my dad do the same to my mum. That's what I knew. I didn't know there could be another way for a man and a woman. You showed me there was. I love you and I'm so sorry. Please, please say you forgive me again!'

He collapsed back on the pillows.

Leaning towards his ear, Nana began to whisper something. Her normally stern features were soft as the tears streamed down her wrinkled face. It felt like such a private moment that I turned to leave the room, but Baba suddenly started up again, ranting, swearing and punching the air. I thought it looked as if he were fighting Death. He was refusing to give up on life, but as I watched him croaking incomprehensively away, I realised that life was giving up on him.

Then I felt Uncle Salman at my side.

'I think it's time. Come, let's say goodbye.'

Like a cat on a thin branch, he walked slowly and carefully towards Baba and kissed him on his forehead. I followed him, though my legs were shaking.

'Goodbye, Baba, I love you,' I said, as I pressed my trembling lips on Baba's forehead, before Mama and Uncle Telman moved in and crowded the bedside to do the same.

My heart sank as I watched through a gap between the adults as Baba's life trickled away moment by moment, until… nothing.

We stood there in silence for a few moments; then suddenly the house became noisy. Nana was giving instructions to my uncles to turn Baba's bed towards Mecca. Phone calls were made, neighbours were summoned. Soon the house was full of people.

In preparation for the burial, Baba's body was washed

by a person called a *murdashir* in our back garden. That was
when I learnt what Nana really meant by saying 'may the
murdashir wash your face', when she saw people kissing or
women in revealing clothes on the TV. It was a curse.

When the *murdashir* was finished, my uncles carried
Baba's body to the drawing room. He was covered with
a white sheet, his bony silhouette outlined through the
cloth. The body seemed to be resting on something sturdy,
raised off the ground, like planks, but I was not sure if it
was a coffin.

I was told to place small pillows and mats around the
sides of the drawing room. For once, I welcomed rushing
around on various errands. I would rather be busy than
sitting, watching Baba's lifeless body. The drawing room
filled up fast. Neighbours, relatives and strangers arrived
and sat in a large circle in the room, to weep and mourn.
Endless cups of tea were made and offered to people when
they came out. I noticed that Nana was not crying anymore.
She was too busy barking commands at everyone.

'Telman, go and buy fifty kilos of meat. Ask them to
give you some soft bits. We are going to make dolma.'
She handed him a roll of cash. She had been saving it up
for months now, especially for this day, by sewing dresses
whilst Baba slept.

'Sevda, when the meat is here, take out the soft bits for
dolma and stew the bony bits for kalapir,' she instructed a
relative, who had volunteered to help cook for the guests.

Nana also had to greet the endless stream of people
and usher them into the drawing room. I watched her
effortlessly switch between tasks.

'Welcome, welcome, yes, I know, isn't this awful? He

wasn't even sixty yet. Still so young. Come through to this room.'

'Let me try your halva. It's a good consistency. You've added enough flour and butter, but it needs more sugar. Yes, good, keep stirring. I'll ask someone to fetch rose water to make it more aromatic.'

'Polad, so how much will his gravestone cost? Don't forget, it's your uncle. I want the best quality stone, enough for *sardaba*. We need a big family grave. While I'm at it, I might as well prepare my own.'

'Don't just stand there, Gulush. Make yourself useful and get some water for the kettle. Keep plenty of boiled water ready so we can brew fresh tea quickly.'

Caught up in the moment, I was delighted to greet relatives I had not seen in years. However, as other girls my age bustled into my grandparents' bedroom for some privacy from adults, I realised I was enjoying the occasion and pangs of guilt pressed heavily down on my heart. I scolded myself.

'You should be crying too. You loved Baba, didn't you?'

'They are going to bury him first thing tomorrow morning,' I overheard someone saying. I gasped. I, his granddaughter, had not yet paid my respects. I had not been to the drawing room myself, recently. There were plenty of spare hands around to keep Nana from needing mine. I should go and cry before they took his body away, I decided.

It was the custom for someone to lead a crying session. As I walked into the drawing room, I realised that it was Mama's turn. She sat on a small stool, which raised her slightly above the rest of the women dressed in black. I hesitated by the door while Mama spoke through her tears.

'My dear father, why, why did you leave us so early? Your strength, your spirit, your courage, they are our inspiration. We'll make you proud. You'll never leave our hearts.'

I slowly approached the place where Mama was sitting, close to Baba's covered body. The room was packed, with no spare cushions, but two women, who may have recognised me, shuffled away to make space for me, next to Mama, in the large, tight circle. Sinking down, I wished I could cry. I tried to summon memories of Baba, to feel the loss, but to start with all I felt was relief that I did not have to look after him anymore, followed again by guilt for feeling that way. I noticed several women were watching me expectantly. I lowered my head to the floor, so that they could not see my face and started wailing, as Mama had done.

'Baba, why did you leave us?' I let false sobbing shake my body. 'Oh Baba, how much I miss you!'

I continued to sob, until I felt Mama pulling me up by the arm and guiding me towards the door, as I cupped my hands to my face, pretending I was still mourning. She dragged me into the corridor. It was only then that I saw her face and realised she was furious with me.

'Never, ever, do that again. Do you hear me? Never throw such a performance in front of other people!'

I felt shame flood through me, turning my face a burning red. If Mama had realised I was faking it, then everyone else must have done so too. I hid in my grandparents' bedroom for the rest of that afternoon. An unexpected period, with stomach cramps, miraculously gave me an excuse to lie in bed and chat weakly to other girls who looked in on me.

Gradually, the house became quieter, but I stayed put. It had been a long day, so when Nana entered the bedroom, I pretended to be asleep. It did not work.

'Go, lock the entrance door, Gulush,' she said. She sounded so tired, crawling into Baba's bed, which my uncles had returned to my grandparents' bedroom before the visitors arrived that morning.

As I went downstairs, I pictured Baba's body, still lying in the drawing room and I wished they had buried him today. The thought of sharing a house with his corpse gave me chills. I locked the door and dashed back into what was now Nana's bedroom. It took me a long while to get to sleep, with Nana sobbing quietly by my side.

★★★

Next morning, as I stood mesmerised by the ranks of crying women in the drawing room, I wondered if they were all truly sad that Baba had gone. Or were they grieving their own losses?

Their sadness pervaded the air. I was feeling lost and empty standing in the doorway, when Great Uncle Hussein flung our front door open and strode in with a group of other men waiting behind him. As soon as the women heard him proclaim: 'Allahuma salli ala Muhammad wa Ali Muhammad,' they parted like a wave, allowing him the space to walk over and stand by Baba's body. The crying subsided while Great Uncle Hussein recited a prayer from the Koran. Only when he had finished did the rest of the men, led by my uncles, enter the room.

Baba was indeed lying in an open coffin. Without

taking off the sheets draped over him, the men secured the sides of the coffin, and hoisted it onto their shoulders. Then they walked proudly out, as if they were carrying a king on his throne. Everyone followed the procession into the street, where one of our large carpets lay on the dusty ground. The men lowered Baba's body in the coffin and stood facing Uncle Hussein.

'Allahu Akbar,' intoned Great Uncle Hussein.

All the men knelt on the carpet and pressed their foreheads to the ground. Great Uncle Hussein spoke again, and they all stood up.

'Allahu Akbar,' they proclaimed, then knelt again in smooth synchronisation, as if they had practiced these moves for weeks.

Great Uncle Hussein towered over them, like a puppeteer, pulling invisible strings with his lilting voice.

Huddled with some of the female mourners by the entrance gate, I held my breath in awe. Eventually, the men lifted the coffin and put it in the back of a large truck. My uncles climbed up and sat next to Baba, while other male relatives and neighbours piled into their cars. I tried to follow, but someone pulled me back.

'Only men go to the cemetery today.'

I was shocked. How could Mama and Nana stand crying but not make any attempt to follow Baba to his final resting place? I never got to ask such questions. As soon as the dust on the road had settled, the women were ushered into a large military marquee that had been hired and erected that morning, blocking one end of our street. Normally, during a wake, men would gather in the marquee to drink tea, while women cried indoors.

Apart from a gentle buzz of conversation as we arranged ourselves along the tables therein, the atmosphere was subdued. Our guests did not stint themselves, however, as they piled their plates with the salads, cheeses and breads from platters waiting on the tables. I looked around the five long tables with the loyal relatives and close neighbours who had taken turns to mourn in the drawing room and help around tirelessly. They chewed enthusiastically and drank the cherry compote that Nana had made the previous summer. As some young men served *kalapir* and *dolma* from heavy trays, women turned towards Khatira *Khala*, the cook Nana hired to prepare food for 300 people a day, to show their appreciation. Nana spent a lot of money to buy the best produce available; as per custom, friends and relatives made donations to support the family.

My crowded mind made me feel tired and without any appetite. I wished I was closer to Mama or Nana who were surrounded by guests. I sat next to Amaliya *Khala*, who ruffled my hair and spooned dolma on my plate.

'Don't be sad. We will all die one day,' she said, as if that would reassure me.

★★★

The women mourners continued to cry in the drawing room for the next three days. I became used to their wailings and heart-wrenching complaints about Baba leaving us so soon.

'Gulush, tell Nana the cars are ready,' Uncle Telman called from the bottom of the stairs on the third day.

There was no need to tell her. Nana was already

walking down the stairs, along with Mama and a long procession of women. Outside, we all climbed into the cars of our neighbours and relatives, ready for departure within minutes. I squeezed into Mirza *Dayi*'s car and practically sat on someone's lap, along with four much larger women.

At the cemetery, Great Uncle Hussein was already reciting the Koran as the procession of women approached. The grave was covered by a large marble stone. Nana poured some rose water into her palm, sprinkled it on the grave and then splashed it on her face, where it mingled with her silent tears. Then the little silver jug was passed around the tight circle.

The smell of the rose water felt comforting, although the women's cries were wearing me out. Since my charade in the drawing room, I had made no attempt to cry. Now, feeling numb, I wandered away to pick flowers. Occasionally, I found snails. I nudged one gently with the delicate stem of a daisy and it retreated into its shell.

When the ceremony was finally over, I left my flowers on the ground because we were not allowed to bring anything home from the cemetery. I remember Nana saying, 'If you bring home even a small stone from a cemetery, you might bring home death.' I was not going to take that risk.

Nana had drummed it into me, from an early age, that I must always follow the rules. They prescribed everything we did in life. Now, squashed between several neighbours in the car, I distracted myself by thinking about some of those rules.

If someone sneezed once, you must wait for a while before setting off anywhere – two sneezes were a good omen. No nail-cutting in the night, or in a place you have never slept before – it could shorten your life. Always throw water and candies after people who are going away, to wish them luck. Spilled salt always means a fight. Even a millimetre of garlic shell on a floor is a sign that conflict is brewing. If you run into someone carrying an empty bucket, it signifies looming misfortune. If your right ear turns red, someone is saying good things about you – that is not true if your left ear burns. If your right palm is itching, you will come into some money, but an itching left palm means that money is running out.

The car stopped outside our front gates and the smell of cooking wafted across our garden. I could hardly jump out of the car fast enough, when I saw the giant pans of food steaming and bubbling above the burning logs.

This time the women went straight to the marquee. Since none of the men were around, they were able to gobble up platefuls of pilau and stewed meat, until they felt replenished. Then, to my horror, they settled in the drawing room, again.

That night I had a dream.

I was in the garden. It was pitch black. I could hardly make out the silhouettes of the trees. In front of me I felt the thick trunk of the old persimmon tree. The earth on the other side of the tree was dark and fertile. A wisp of grey started rising from it.

Frozen in terror, the hairs rising on the back of my neck, I watched as the smoke emerging from the ground grew like a plant into Baba's torso.

'Gulush, I miss you. Come with me,' he said.

He looked well now and younger, just as I remembered him from my earlier childhood.

165

'Come with me. It's so lonely here. I miss you. Come!'

Then Nana's voice whispered in my ear, 'Whatever you do, you must never, ever follow a dead person if they call you when you're sleeping. You simply won't wake up.'

Speechless, I watched Baba smile.

His voice became more insistent.

'Come with me, little Gulush. I know that, of all those people, you love me the most. Come!'

I saw his hand, smooth and thin, extending towards me, but I couldn't move! I couldn't move…

Then I woke up, to the sound of my own shrieking. Nana was shaking me roughly and I realised with relief that I was in her bedroom. As soon as I told her my dream, she said, 'Go dress. We are going to see a *Mullah* to dedicate a reading of the Koran to your Baba.'

We paid a *Mullah* three rubles to pray for Baba's spirit to rest in peace, but that night I found I still could not sleep. Every time I closed my eyes, fear flooded me, whispering a terrifying warning: He will return. He will take you away. You know this. He still loves you, so, so much.

I spent many hours forcing my eyes to stay wide open, fearing for my life. I was so tired in those days that my smile faded away. Even when my friends and young relatives visited us, I no longer felt happy. My grief was now far more appropriate for the occasion, I thought, as I caught someone's understanding glance.

★★★

The weeping ritual continued until the seventh day after the burial, when we had another visit to the cemetery. I still could not cry. I even tried pinching myself to make tears appear, but nothing happened. Something inside of me was hard as a wall, and I could not break through it.

After that seventh day of mourning the weeks kept the same pattern for a while. Every Thursday we had a gathering to commemorate Baba, with the women huddled in the drawing room sobbing then having a meal with tea and halva, whilst the men gathered in the garden with my uncles.

I could not stand being amongst the women anymore, my sleep was still troubled, but I was not supposed to go into the garden either. Instead, I hid in Uncle Salman's bedroom and eavesdropped on the men's conversations over their endless glasses of black tea. Because our family was in mourning and we were not supposed to watch television or listen to music for forty days, I had no idea what was going on in the wider world. It was like being in limbo. The men shared their predictable concerns over whether the Kapaz football team would win their next game, and more interestingly, their worries about the political climate in the country. I heard that the war with Armenia was escalating. Also, there were anti-Soviet protests in Baku. The Popular Front, the first opposition party, formed a year earlier, was growing in strength and influence. Some men seemed to be concerned about the mounting disgruntlement with the Soviet regime, while others were pleased that the people were finally waking up and opposing decades of oppression. I did not know what to make of these conversations.

The fortieth day was marked with another ceremony at the cemetery whilst the neighbours erected the marquee on the street again and large quantities of food were prepared in the front garden to await our return. At the cemetery I was shocked to see Baba's photograph smiling at me from the marble stone, next to his beloved son Javan. He was the same age as in my dream. I tried to think about how much I had loved him, as the women wept over his grave, but again I found it easier to slip away to find a snail in the flowers. Though I felt like I was failing him, not being able to cry, the hard wall growing inside me seemed as strong as ever.

14.

CRYSTAL RAIN

Kirovabad, Azerbaijan S.S.R., 1989

My summer holidays were spent soaked in the tears of others and watching the gradual disintegration of my family. It was as if Baba had been the glue that kept the whole family together. Two months after the funeral, Uncle Telman and his wife bought a flat at the far end of Lenin Avenue. On occasional visits to their flat, I saw that their life seemed more settled without Nana's constant interventions. Then Mama and her new family moved out into a nearby rental. Even if they were keen to have me with them, I could not leave Nana behind alone, given that she needed practical help around the house. Besides, Mama's life was busier than ever: she had joined the Popular Front, the opposition party, and had got a job as a journalist at the local newspaper. So, I finally decided to follow Sevil's advice, after Jalil beat Mama up, and leave them to their own devices. As to Uncle Salman, he spent most of his time lurking in teahouses with his fellow unemployed friends.

Living virtually alone with Nana was not easy. Her way of grieving the loss of her husband and the desertion of her children was to rant and complain. When school resumed in September, I felt elated. Seeing my friends again provided a welcome break from the heavy atmosphere at home and filled me with new hope and excitement.

One balmy, late September afternoon, Leyla and I strolled at a leisurely pace home on the long route, to give ourselves extra time to catch up on news. I enjoyed feeling the light breeze stroke the skin of my bare arms as I listened to Leyla's tales of her summer holidays. We paused our conversation when we reached The Bottle House, and as usual, we stopped to admire it. It was a local icon. The owner had transformed the outside of his home into a work of art, made entirely of glass bottles – thousands of them. Translucent in the sun, the bottles were carefully arranged into colourful mosaics of words and portraits that reflected and refracted the light as it passed through the walls of the building made of bottles. Green oak trees, with a touch of yellow and light brown, next to the house, added the dappled shadows of their waving branches to the effect.

That street was quiet, but we could hear a hum of voices in the distance and puzzled over a whirring sound, which grew stronger as we sauntered closer to the city centre.

'Maybe it's the Popular Front again,' Leyla speculated. 'Did you see the news about them forcing the Supreme Council to adopt the law on Economic Sovereignty for Azerbaijan? If we take charge of our oil and gas, the next step is independence.' Her tone was annoyingly knowledgeable, and I wondered whether she was repeating what her dad, a dean at the local institute, talked about at home.

I too had heard speculation about political changes in other parts of the Soviet Union, but campaigns of civil resistance against Soviet rule, pushing for change in the Baltic Republics, were too far away to affect us, I thought. Even local events in our capital, Baku, where the Azerbaijan Popular Front organised regular anti-Soviet protest meetings in the main square seemed unlikely to make a difference.

Turning onto the fountain square we saw that assembled in front of the City Council House was a huge crowd. The imposing, grey edifice of the building looked solid and impregnable. Giant letters, proclaiming 'long life to the Communist Party' in Azerbaijani and Russian, stretched across both sides of the building. Here the air felt thin, as if there was not enough oxygen, so everyone was holding their breath. The crowd seemed restless, with mutterings and shuffling of feet and there was agitation in the voices of some who were shouting from its midst.

Tentatively, we stood on the fringes of the gathering, quiet as mice. Someone from the Tribune was speaking, and I strained to hear. To my surprise, it was a female voice. Was a woman leading this demonstration? I stood on tiptoes to have a better look.

A woman in her late thirties stood on the podium, in a neat grey jacket and long black skirt. Her dark shoulder-length hair framed her face and, even from this distance, I could make out the shine of her red lipstick. My eyebrows arched up, as I tugged Leyla's sleeve. Her cat-like smile told me she already knew who it was. Nigar Bayramovna was the mother of our classmate, Asif. Her voice boomed through the crackling PA system, across the square: 'We demand freedom! We demand the restoration of the historic name of our city. Enough is enough. Every time the

171

Russians occupy us, they rob us of our legacy. First, during the Russian Empire days, they took away our proud city's original name – Ganja – and changed it to Elizabethpol. Our ancestors fought courageously to reclaim it and our independence in 1918! That didn't last. We were invaded again, by the Soviets. Stalin forced the name of Kirovabad on us, to honour his friend Kirov. But who is that Kirov to us? I ask you that!'

By now, she was squealing with indignation, just like her son Asif did at school whenever he talked about politics. 'I propose we unite and demand that our true legacy should be honoured and restored.'

Many men watching in their grey solemn suits were balling their fists and nodding approvingly, even though it was a woman speaking from the Tribune. I noticed that the men were standing shoulder to shoulder and the only gaps in the crowd were around the women. Unlike that brute who groped me on the bus, these men seemed to be respectfully giving them space.

I studied the women in the heart of the crowd with open curiosity. Were they single? What did their families make of their political activism? In my household, women were not allowed to join men at the table for a meal, let alone stand shoulder to shoulder with them in a public square. I thought it was brave, even reckless of them to be in the centre of the events. Looking at their clothes, I tried to pinpoint whether they were from wealthy families or not. In particular, one woman in a dark blue dress caught my eye. The dress was so like one of Mama's favourites. I looked up from its folds at her face. It was Mama! What was she doing here? I elbowed my way towards her. People murmured in disapproval, as if I had broken their trance.

'Mama, what are you doing here?' I hissed when I reached her.

'The same as you,' she said.

'I was just passing by on the way from school,' I said defensively. I was actually too young, at fourteen, to demonstrate. I expected her to tell me off for being there, but she did not seem to care.

'This is our future. Watch carefully, you are witnessing history in the making.'

I did not understand her then, I felt annoyed. Now wedged in the thick of the crowd, I worried how I would get back home on time. Nana would be furious if I was back late. I did not want to make history. I had homework to do. Rising on tiptoes, I tried to locate Leyla. She was on the edge of the crowd. I squeezed Mama's hand goodbye and headed towards Leyla.

'Did you see him?' Leyla's voice was a purr next to my ear. I looked around. 'By the podium. It's Asif.' She pointed to the front of the building, where Nigar Bayramovna stood on the platform.

Trying to spot him, I scanned the crowd without much success. I could not see him but felt sure he was going to be full of himself at school the next day. I sighed imagining him, the centre of attention again, sharing the news, words bubbling like river-water from his mouth.

A large clock striking nearby made Leyla and I realise how late it was. I felt too restless to wait for a bus, and sprinted home, taking a shortcut through a slightly deserted area, which added more urgency to my step. I made it home later than usual, out of breath and dishevelled, to find tea already on the table and Nana sitting in her bedroom with Baba's photo on her lap. She seemed suspicious as she peered at the wall clock but was too wrapped up in her own grief to press it, as I rushed to wash my hands before eating, my heart racing. Nana was not likely to approve of any anti-Soviet sentiments since she still adored Stalin and considered him to be the real man.

★★★

When the summer heat was replaced by cool weather, with harsh gusts of wind, walking home from school was not so much fun. The oak trees lining the fountain square were turning deep brown and shedding their leaves. Leyla still liked to find out what was going on in the city centre and I enjoyed her company. It helped me unwind from the pressures of schoolwork and chores at home.

One day, we were talking about our anatomy class, the one we had been waiting for for about two years. Chapters forty-one and forty-two of our biology textbooks were legendary; they related to the male and female anatomy. Discussing, or even thinking about your genitals was deemed to be shameful, and people acted as if they did not have them or had no idea what those parts of the body produced.

'I had been looking forward to this class. We barely spent three minutes on those two chapters taken together. I wanted to know the details, the right words to use, that sort of thing. Nana always makes it sound so… disgusting. She makes me cringe,' I said, shuddering.

'She's just an old widow woman,' said Leyla, as we

reached the city centre. 'What can she know about human anatomy?'

Another crowd was in the fountain square, but instead of facing the council house they were forming a massive circle in the centre between two large fountains, the remnants of the Imperial days. The few brightly clad women interspersed amongst the majority of grey-suited, stiff-backed men, like gems in a cave rock.

I turned to ask Leyla what was going on, but she just shrugged her shoulders.

'Let's go find out,' she said and headed straight for them.

I hesitated, stepping from foot to foot, before I charged after her to catch up. We found a gap in the circle and peered in. Four middle-aged men, dressed in an intermediate shade of brown camouflage trousers and warm overcoats with thick jackets and furry collars, were facing in the direction of the council house and chanting:

'*Azadliq! Azadliq! Azadliq!*'

'Freedom! Freedom! Freedom!' From what, I was not sure.

There was a small khaki-coloured military tent erected near these men, big enough for several people to sleep in. Were they planning to stay overnight? Unthinkable, given how cold the nights were in November. I pulled my woolly coat tighter around my neck and gaped at the men in surprise. Two of them had black stretchy hats, pulled down to their bushy eyebrows. They did not look that different to the other men in the crowd and their stubbly faces did not give me any clues as to their possible purpose or occupation.

A tall, black-moustached man standing next to us

quietly remarked to his silver-haired companion: 'They've vowed to stay on hunger strike until Azerbaijan gets its independence back. Like that's going to happen. This is what comes of that Gorbachov's talk of 'perestroika'. They'd probably be shot by now, if Stalin was alive.'

His words reminded me of Nana's views. My heart started pounding as I noticed the older man's hands had started shaking where he clutched his walking stick. Was he frightened too?

What if Leyla and I ended up in trouble, for being associated with these people? I glanced at her, but her expression was one of excitement rather than concern. The four men in the middle stopped their chanting and walked the full radius of the circle, trying to gain the people's support.

'Etibar Mammadov has been arrested. We need to unite and demand that the government releases him. He stood up to this regime, now it's our turn to stand up for him. Our opposition forces need their leader. The Popular Front is still young,' they variously pleaded with the crowd.

'Why do you care?' someone shouted. 'If you're not careful, you'll rot in prison with him.'

I turned around to see the snarl on the face of the speaker. One of the protesters inside the circle fixed his gaze, as if in disbelief, then walked slowly closer to where the young man was standing. Time itself seemed to freeze at that moment, as we all stared at the protestor, in his rough trousers and well-worn warm jacket, fire in his eyes. He seemed huge to me, this man who dared to speak against the Soviet regime. The speaker shifted uncomfortably as the protestor stood right up close to him.

'I'm doing this for my children. For their future. One day, you will all understand!' His clear tones rang across the square. Then he reached to pat the youth on his shoulder before turning away back to the centre of the circle to resume the chant.

'Those are brave men, aren't they?' Leyla said. Her eyes were shining with something like devotion.

'No,' I whispered fiercely. 'They are idiots, and we must go.' I pulled at her arm. 'No one in their right mind would do such a thing.'

'I still think they are so courageous,' she replied.

'Whatever, the show is over for us. Come on,' I said as I propelled her away.

It was one thing to mingle anonymously with a large crowd, but quite another to be possibly caught on camera watching a defiant protest. We walked on, a tense silence between us, until we reached the bus stop where we usually parted.

'Brave,' Leyla repeated.

I shook my head but smiled and we hugged goodbye. She could be so stubborn.

My bus arrived promptly, and I even managed to get a seat by a window. As the bus whizzed by grey buildings and naked trees, the image of the men chanting '*Azadliq*' flashed in front of my eyes. I had never seen anyone stand up to the government like that before but knew that Nana's parents were supposed to have been revolutionaries of sorts. She sometimes recounted how her mother had been one of the women who rejected the hijab. She had even thrown her headscarf off in public. Apparently, my great grandmother had also wielded a gun and stood up to men. She had died when Nana was only ten and her husband was exiled, first to Siberia and then to Iran, for his political activism. This had resulted in my resolve to stay clear of politics, unlike Leyla, who felt fervently patriotic.

It was amazing that we had remained friends for so many years. We were complete opposites, inside and out: Leyla, tall, dark-skinned, brown-eyed and broad-shouldered; me, petite, pale, with chestnut hair and green-blue eyes. Leyla had total confidence in herself and the world around her, whereas I saw it as an obstacle course to be negotiated carefully and, for the most part, quietly. I never dared to speak my mind, something that would never occur to Leyla. Whether you liked it or not, she always said what she thought.

I was the first to jump off the bus when it arrived outside the textile factory where Nana had spent so many years of her youth sweating over a mechanised loom, and nearly bumped into the irrepressible Svetlana *Khala*, the wife of one of Mama's cousins.

'Gulush,' she exclaimed. I had not spoken to her for ages, so it was most alarming when she grabbed my arm and started to lead me away from the bus stop. There was such an urgency and determination to her stride, so unusual for her, that I did not even ask after her two daughters. When we were out of anyone's earshot, she turned to face me.

'Did you see him?' Her periwinkle blue eyes scanned my face for a reaction.

'See who?'

'Your father, of course! Didn't anyone tell you at home? He is one of the men who is on hunger strike in the city centre. It's in all the newspapers. Here.' She shoved a crumpled copy of the *Voice of Ganja* newspaper into my hands. 'I have to go now.' Her voice sounded breathless with excitement. 'I thought that Rosa *Khala* wouldn't tell you. That's why I waited for you.' She patted me on the head, as if I were still a small child. 'You poor little thing. Come see me if you need me again, Gulush.' And before I had time to process the information or ask her any questions, she gave me a brief hug and hurried away.

I stood motionless, in the middle of the pavement where she had left me. I scarcely noticed the next bus screeching to a halt nearby and disgorging its passengers, until they started to push past me. Then it was as if their questioning eyes were all focused on me. I flushed crimson and made myself cross the street and walk home.

My mind was overwhelmed with questions, whirling like clothes inside a washing machine. Why did she tell me? Would she be in trouble with my family, if they knew? Would I be in trouble with my family if I dared to approach my father? I felt so confused. How could my dad be one of those four men? Was it the one who claimed he was doing it for his children's future? My future? I wished I had taken a closer look at them. He was not safe there. He might well be brave, but that would not stop the government from harming him, would it?

As I approached the house, still shaking, I hid the newspaper in my school bag, greeted Nana then quickly ran outside into the garden to where I could scrutinise it without being seen. I was disappointed to find the small section on the demonstration had no photographs, just names, but one of them was my dad's, Nizami Guliyev!

When Nana called for me, I nearly fell off the old barrel

I was sitting on. I carefully removed the page, folded it and slid it into a textbook and tossed the remainder into a bush.

Evening turned into night, but time crawled for me. I walked from room to room, unable to concentrate on anything. If Nana asked any questions, I mumbled something incomprehensible, avoiding her inquisitive eyes. Agitation burned me from the inside out. Why hadn't I looked properly at their faces? I should have recognised him! Nana always said I looked like him. Would he have recognised me?

I imagined how we might have spoken together, despite the crowds, despite the situation. If only I had been paying attention and not thinking of my own safety. This thought, of my selfishness, of this lost chance, tightened my chest. The air in the house seemed to close in on me. I raced into the garden to my safe space behind the chicken coop and allowed myself some hot, quiet tears of regret. A few minutes later I heard Nana bleating from the house. Wiping my face dry with my underskirt, I painted on my smile and trotted back, the picture of a dutiful granddaughter, whilst my mind fermented with rebellion. Tomorrow, after classes, I vowed, I would go back, no matter the risks.

★★★

The next morning, after a dream tossed sleep, I went to school early and waited for Leyla with a thumping heart, desperate to share my news. The school entrance door was still locked, so I stood outside, shivering in the cold, alone. Had my dad and the other men survived the night in that thin tent, weakened from lack of food?

I only noticed Leyla when she tapped me on the shoulder, and I whirled around to see her grinning face. I kept nothing back, telling her the facts and my regrets, even letting her see my tears. Drawing me away from the entrance, where others were arriving now and looking curiously at me, she whispered gently: 'See, I told you they were brave.'

For once I did not mind her being right. She even volunteered to come with me after school to find out which of the hunger strikers was my dad.

I found it so hard to pay attention in any of my classes that day. Two of the teachers even warned me I might get a *dvoika*, but I did not care.

As soon as the school bell rang out, Leyla and I went sprinting towards the fountain square. Weighed down by heavy textbooks and my sports kit, always panting paces behind Leyla, I wished I had made more effort in PE myself.

I sighed with relief when I saw the crowd was still there.

Eager to see what was happening, we slipped through the gaps, right into the heart of the mostly grey-clad mass. My chest was tight from anticipation as well as from running. Impatiently, I half pushed myself through the final gap and almost fell onto the hard flagstones. Then a wave of nausea swept over me. The tent was completely closed up. The only man visible was a self-important looking policeman.

He was circling the perimeter of the now taped off area, ordering people to disperse. Where was my dad? Was he all right? I wanted to rush to the policeman and demand that he tell me, but Leyla put her arms round me. I clung to her as we strained to hear the conversations of the men around us.

I had to fight myself not to cry as I heard first that they were not dead, then that they were weakening and had had to rest in the tent.

'As soon as they go unconscious, they'll be carted off. Mark my words,' one man said harshly.

I could not believe it. I hated myself at that moment. I had missed the precious, possibly only, chance to meet my dad because of my own cowardice. Regret started to corrode my reason and I let the tears start to fall. I should have stayed before. I should have come back in the night. I tensed up, as my senses were telling me to run past the policeman, into the circle, into the tent – my reason, and Leyla's arms holding me a little tighter now, told me no.

'You were right, Gulush,' she whispered. 'We should not be here. Your dad wouldn't want you to suffer, would he?'

I nodded. We stood there a little while longer but when more police arrived, I let her lead me away, as I felt my mind shut down. Leyla sat with me on a bench near the bus stop until the bus arrived.

'Ring me if you need to,' she said. 'See you tomorrow.'

I did not remember how I got home, or anything else about that day. My dad and his fellow patriots continued their hunger strike for another two days, four days in all. I caught sight of him on the TV news, when Nana was out, as they were all taken away on stretchers to hospital. The public outcry over this event was so strong that the government, in an unprecedented U-turn, released Etibar Mammadov.

The last I heard was that all four men on the hunger strike had recovered. I hoped that my dad would not put himself at risk again and that we could meet one day.

★★★

For several weeks after this, each time Leyla and I went to peruse the city centre, it seemed as if the number of demonstrators was growing rapidly. Soon the fountain square was regularly full to the brim and the crowd spread out into the side road. Leyla and I had to negotiate the crowds to get to our bus stops.

We often stopped to listen to the speeches. Nana knew of the traffic chaos the demonstrations were causing so did not question my lateness.

Asif's mum, Nigar Bayramovna, was ever present. There were other voices too, mainly male, who spoke about freedom. Occasionally, I glimpsed Mama's familiar silhouette in the crowd.

As the days became shorter and colder, I once suggested that we change our route home to avoid the demonstrators, but Leyla disagreed.

'How will you be able to join in with Asif if you don't know what is going on? And you, the daughter of a freedom fighter,' she said.

Most days, the atmosphere on the square was solemn, mirroring the grey winter days. I wondered whether my dad's struggle was in vain. Would we ever live to see the day of real breakthrough? Was there any point in these people coming here every day? I did not always understand what they were on about, but it all boiled down to calls for more independence from our Soviet masters. It was ironic that all of this was taking place in front of the city council house. Did the officials join the demonstrations too, or silently watch from their windows? Why did the government tolerate the people's demands for freedom? I did not dare to voice my questions at school, lest someone report me for being unpatriotic or anti-Soviet.

★★★

As the days went by, we got used to our routine detour to watch the demonstrations. We could not go as often because of other activities and the shortening daylight hours, but both Leyla and I enjoyed feeling part of something, even though we were not supposed to be there – until one Tuesday.

Leyla had been telling me about one of her cousin's latest escapades when she stopped suddenly.

'Gulya, do you hear that?'

'Hear what?' I was still laughing when I realised what was missing.

'Where are all the people?' Leyla said. 'I can't hear anyone shouting.'

'But there are people, look,' I said as we reached our destination.

In the late afternoon light, the crowds were bigger than ever before, but packed closer together and a mix of every kind of person, even families.

'We did it!' One voice was joined by many echoing across the square. People started cheering, some even threw their hats in the air and almost danced as they embraced one another. Leyla and I stood on the fringes, bewildered.

'What's happening?' Leyla asked one young man. He smiled broadly and shouted something back, but his reply was drowned by a sudden growl of thunder. Looking up, we saw the sky had quickly darkened and lightning crackled across the sky, some seeming to hit the ground nearby.

'We must go home,' I shouted, as the wind whipped the trees into a dance. We had not a raincoat between us. Leyla turned to answer me, the crowd pressing around us, but the voice of Nigar Bayramovna silenced her, as the rain started to pour down.

'Dear brothers and sisters. Brothers and sisters,' she repeated, as Leyla and I hurried to stand where we could see her on the podium. She was completely untroubled by the rain, though her hair was dripping wet and her outfit already clinging to her.

'Congratulations! We have achieved an important milestone. The name Ganja has been returned to our city. As you may know, it means 'treasure', so let's treasure our heritage. It finally belongs to us.'

I felt the impact of her words in my bones. Suddenly, it did not matter that we were soaked to the skin. Leyla and I started to jump up and down in celebration along with everyone else.

The rain felt like it was washing away the past. It reminded me of Nana's favourite line from our compatriot, 12th century poet Nizami Ganjavi: 'In the hour of adversity be not without hope, for crystal rain falls from black clouds'. People chanted 'Ganja, Ganja' as we all reclaimed the name of our city. For the youth, me and Leyla, it was gaining a part of our cultural identity we had never been allowed to own before.

The rain stopped as suddenly as it started. I breathed in the clean fresh air, saturated with the smell of earth, our earth. I had never felt so close to my home city.

15.

BLACK JANUARY

Ganja, Azerbaijan S.S.R., 1990

Reclaiming the name of our city was only a small step towards independence. Many people refused to work in order to attend demonstrations, which had unsettling effects on our lives, such as a shortage of bread. Every day over the winter school holidays, I went to the local shop and stared at the empty shelves. The shopkeeper would just shrug her shoulders when I asked when a delivery was due.

Next, Nana sent me to the newly opened private bakeries to buy hot scrumptious tandoori bread, but the demand was so great that queues curled around the block like a sleeping snake. The buttery aroma would waft down the street as successive customers walked past those still waiting, carrying their stack of steaming bread away. Sometimes, a flashy GAZ-31 car would pull up next to us and some high official's driver would jump the queue. This was met with a disapproving murmur from the crowd but no direct confrontation. When it got to the point where I was spending up to three hours a day in queues, Nana finally decided we should make our own bread.

Within two weeks of the new year, shelves in the shops looked orphaned. Although there was no organised movement in Ganja, a sizeable proportion of the local proletariat abandoned factories in favour of standing in the winter cold, listening to the freedom speakers. Nana was worried about us starving and acted like we would be back on a ration the size of a matchbox she used to receive as a child when she worked at a match factory. After Baba's cousin generously gifted us a sack of potatoes from his farm in a village, we lived on potato soup for weeks. Nana squirreled away any produce she could buy informally, and possibly illegally, through neighbours whose relatives worked in warehouses and presumably stole some supplies. She had a stash of sugar, rice, plain flour and sunflower oil, but there was no question of her buying any fruit, which used to be a rare treat in wintertime anyway. Even a monthly Soviet ration of sugar lumps, stinky margarine and bony beef was not available any longer; people panic-bought anything that remained in the abandoned shops. Nana constantly cursed the anti-Soviet movement that created food shortages and her stories of wartime starvation seemed very real to me.

When school resumed on the 15th of January, Nana stopped me from going altogether. She was worried about my safety. Due to the protests, the buses were no longer operating a reliable service and would sometimes stop long before our area. Although I was willing to walk, many of the teachers and pupils were absent or late, so lessons were usually disrupted.

'This country is in an explosive state, Gulush,' Nana cautioned, 'and I don't want my precious granddaughter in any danger.'

She was right, of course. On the 9ᵗʰ of January, Armenia had announced it was annexing Nagorno-Karabakh. We were at war. Uncle Salman showed me why this was so controversial. The area was right inside our borders. The Armenians in Nagorno-Karabakh wanted to access Armenia's budget and vote in its elections and had turned against Azerbaijan.

This shift of allegiance was met with outrage in the rest of Azerbaijan. It led to pogroms against Armenians in Baku and other places a week later. I was shocked by what had happened. I could not comprehend how people who used to be regarded as our friends could so suddenly be viewed as our enemies. The varied negative reactions of my family mirrored that across Azerbaijan.

Nana declared: 'I'm not surprised. Armenians are fed hatred of us true Azerbaijanis with their mother's milk!'

Mama pointed to distant history and how the Armenian population had betrayed Javad Khan, the ruler of Ganja in the eighteenth century, by opening the city gates to its enemies.

All I could think of in response was the kindness of my Armenian music teacher. Luckily, she had relocated to Russia, so was a safe distance away from the events. It was hard for me when I realised that I was never likely to see her again.

★★★

While marooned at home, I helped Nana with chores and accompanied her to the bazaar. The television was my only source of comfort, although watching the news caused increasing anxiety and confusion within the family. Just like with the Armenian situation, our views differed.

Although the Berlin Wall had fallen several months before, Uncle Telman's wife Sevil could not stop talking about her childhood in Berlin where her dad served as part of the Soviet troops. The widespread reports of economic disparity between West and East Germany surprised her, she said, because she remembered life in Berlin as prosperous and comfortable.

Meanwhile, the events in the Baltic Republics usually sparked Mama's memories of Latvia when she first lived there with Jalil. Her eyes sparkled when she admired how united and unique Latvia, Lithuania and Estonia had remained throughout the Soviet rule.

'Do you remember how they formed a two-million long human chain to protest against the Soviets last year? That's what I call solidarity. What could Moscow do against that many humans stretched for several hundred kilometres between Estonia and Lithuania?' She spoke fervently to Uncle Telman during a rare family gathering, when everyone huddled around a cast iron heater.

Uncle Telman shook his head but before he could say anything Nana got irate.

'You are all idiots. This country needs another Stalin to put everything right.'

I did not know what to make of these conversations. They neither explained why the Soviet Union was plunged into chaos nor alleviated my concerns for the future.

★★★

One morning the TV stopped working. No matter what Nana and I did the screen stayed blank, so Nana decided we should go to the open-air bazaar instead. She picked up several bags, put her coat on and waited for me impatiently at the door. Were we safe walking to the bazaar for half an hour, I wondered?

It was a cold January morning. I did not really want to be at the bazaar. It was nothing new. I dragged along behind Nana, lost in thoughts about the current political situation, as she skilfully examined all the local farm produce on sale. There were mounds of fruit and vegetables: crisp apples, potatoes and onions alongside more expensive items, such as walnuts, chestnuts and pomegranates. Everything was neatly arranged and every stall holder eager to please, until the moment you said 'no thank you', when their tired faces fell back into a frown.

Despite myself, the sights, scents and sounds gradually worked their magic on me. Here in the fresh winter air, life was bustling on, as if everything was still normal. Nana bought me a couple of wrinkled apples, as a reward for being her donkey. As I munched the soft flesh, even the traders' loud shouting to attract customers felt almost welcome. It was fun to watch Nana stop from time to time and haggle with a vendor.

'How much do you charge for potatoes?'

'Five rubles, *Khala*, they were grown in Dashkasan. Fluffy and soft, you won't regret buying them.' The young man pulled his hat down over his ears and rubbed his gloved hands.

'Do you think I was born yesterday? These are not from Dashkasan! Tell your tales to someone else.'

191

'*Khala*, in the name of Allah, they are from Dashkasan! But, just for you, they are four rubles!'

Nana shook her head. Smiling, she started to turn away, but the youth would not give up.

'Three and a half, if you take the whole bucket!' he called out. My heart sank as Nana reached for her purse.

The straps of the shopping bags were already starting to cut into my hands. My arms felt painfully stretched, my shoulders were drooping with tiredness. How would I carry that bucket as well?

I reached out my hand, about to try and dissuade her, when the buzz of normality around us stopped. A long procession of men slowly marched into the bazaar carrying huge bunches of red carnations. Nana and I had no idea why. People often gifted each other red carnations, but we had never seen so many being carried like this before.

'Who will give us more?' one of the men shouted.

Several of the traders came to hand more bundles of the blood red flowers to these men as they moved through the bazaar.

As an elder lady, Nana could ask questions of anyone, even men. She waylaid one of the carnation gatherers by grabbing his sleeve.

'What are all those for?'

The young man's lean sad face looked concerned for her.

'You haven't heard, *Khala*? I'm so sorry to be the one to tell you.'

'Tell me what?' Nana replied.

He swallowed and said: 'The Soviets. They killed hundreds of brave Azerbaijani people in Baku, just a few hours ago. We are gathering the flowers to mourn them…'

Nana gasped and let go of his sleeve to cover her mouth.

'Everyone is being asked to donate red carnations to mark the loss of innocent blood.'

'That is why the TV isn't working?' Nana murmured as the young man left to join his fellow collectors.

'Yes,' answered a woman next to us. 'The Soviets blew up the power lines to the TV and radio stations, but they couldn't silence everyone. People came from Baku, I heard. Those bastards killed innocent women and children, as well as men.'

'Why?' Nana croaked.

'Because of the nationalists, that's what I think. It's all the Popular Front's fault. Now Moscow sent tanks to stop the demonstrations. Some people lay on the frosty ground in protest, to stop the tanks from entering the city. The tanks didn't stop…'

Her words chilled me to the bone. Mama was an active member of the Popular Front. Laying in front of a tank and saying 'over my dead body' was exactly the kind of thing Mama and my father would do. Nana was clutching my already burdened arm. I realised she too was fighting back tears. As I took some slow, cool breaths to steady myself, I felt all hope of normality sucked from the air.

'We'd better go, Nana,' I heard myself saying. I sounded so calm.

For once, without comment, Nana let me lead her home.

★★★

Many people, some of whom we knew, headed for Baku from all over the country in the next few days to bury those who had been brave enough to stand up to the regime. Mama had not been one of them, but I did not know about my father. The TV was restored the next day. As we sat in mourning, me, Nana and sometimes neighbours or other family members, watching our people united through grief, I would scan the faces of the crowds hoping to glimpse my dad amongst them.

Thousands carried the ordinary people, made martyrs by this act of aggression, in their coffins to the burial site. Their path was paved with a river of red carnations. Those humble flowers to be worn every January since, in some form or other, to commemorate the events of that day.

Nana's eyes were constantly red, her cheeks sore, from all the crying, since any mention of a young person dying always triggered her memories of her own beloved son Javan. She was repeating the story of how it was snowing flakes the size of a bird's head on the day he died, when it did not usually snow in September, when we heard someone calling from our downstairs hall.

It was our neighbour Mirza *Dayi*. 'Rosa *Khala*, they are coming, they are coming!' he shouted.

Nana scurried towards his voice and I raced after her. Mirza *Dayi* was holding two bottles of sparkling water. They looked somewhat strange: instead of regular round metallic tops, they had corks made of muslin.

'The Soviet tanks are on the way to Ganja, now.' He sounded breathless. 'Dress the girl, in case you have to leave. Make sure you have some spare bread at home.' We stared at him in horror. Nana motioned towards the bottles in his hand.

'Be careful using those. If that explodes in your hand…'

'Of course, of course,' he said impatiently. 'Do you have anything else we can use? I've taken out all the petrol from my car.'

He stood expectantly, his usually immaculate clothes dishevelled and dirty, his jawline tense. Nana pulled her headscarf tighter and led him to the garage, giving him the emergency can of petrol hidden there. As he hurried off, she turned to me and said, 'We must be ready for whatever comes, Gulush. If the Popular Front stands up to the Soviets like they did in Baku, people will be killed.'

I nodded, keeping my head down to hide the tears welling in my eyes, while she bustled to check our stores.

'Mama,' I whispered to myself. Thinking of her made me feel woozy; I buckled over to suppress the scream of panic that was trying to escape from my mouth, reminding myself that there were people in our city who were willing to give up their lives to stop the Soviets. I was the daughter of one of them, so must stand firm too. Still shaking but now determined, I went to help Nana.

Within an hour of our conversation with Mirza *Dayi*, our entire neighbourhood was silent and waiting. When I poked my head out of the iron gates, Nana being too busy to notice, I saw only a few older women watching the empty road for the men, old and young, to return. We had all been told to be ready to run. Protecting the purity of women from the Soviets, and the lives of children, was the community's greatest concern.

Every minute seemed to last an hour since Nana would not let me out of her sight. She insisted that we lie on our beds, fully dressed, in our coats, listening to every sound around us, for most of the afternoon.

At dusk, we sat in silence and watched people mourning the deaths in Baku on TV. A further eight hundred had been listed as injured. Reporters interviewed eyewitnesses who recounted the horrors of that dreadful day, whilst I tortured myself worrying about Mama, as I imagined her being somewhere on the edge of our city with a blunt kitchen knife, trying to stop the troops.

The peaceful darkness outside was suddenly broken with the noise of men shouting, kids squealing and women crying out prayers.

Nana and I hurried towards the crescendo in the street.

'We stopped the tanks! They turned around! They've left our city!'

Everyone was celebrating. People spilled out into the street to watch our heroes hug each other and their families and soon the air was thick with cooking smells.

Initially I found it hard to share everyone's enthusiasm. I just watched them. Was this it? Was this really a victory? Then Nana found me and gave me such a hug, her face beaming, that I relaxed and joined in the party.

***

Unfortunately, I was proved right. That very night, as we slept, dreaming of freedom and sweet pastries, the Soviet troops sneaked into our city via a back road. Nana and I were woken early by neighbours, as news of this outrage passed from household to household.

Soviet stealth may have avoided casualties, the strength of their presence made open resistance pointless, but it was still an invasion. The city centre had been filled with tanks and armed Soviet soldiers. USSR President Mikhail Gorbachev imposed a curfew on the city – the streets were to be patrolled by the military and no one was allowed to leave their homes after midnight.

The first time I saw a tank parked in front of the *Univermag* department store, I was impressed by its dimensions and skilful construction. I had never seen one in real life, just in Soviet movies on TV. They seemed so much larger now, like evil green monsters, towering over us. A line of them stood guard, not far from the Lenin statue, where Leyla and I once sought shade during the demonstrations. The Soviet presence soon ended our after-school adventures. Nana insisted on chaperoning me to and from school.

The changes at school were subtle at first: Asif and several boys stopped wearing their scarlet pioneer scarves. The collars of their white shirts looked naked without the symbolic red flames. I expected our teachers to challenge them, but none did. This non-response encouraged others to 'forget' theirs, until eventually the entire class stopped wearing them, myself included.

This was not just the end of my membership of Young Pioneers, it meant I would not become a member of Komsomol, the youth division of the Communist Party. Soviet structures began to collapse from the bottom up.

★★★

As the spring equinox approached, people's defiance of the Soviet regime and continued anger at the events of Black January were expressed in a lavish and public celebration of the dearly loved spring festival, *Novruz*. We had marked it every year of my life, but always behind closed doors, since the Soviet authorities had not approved of the festival's historic links to ancient Azerbaijani traditions such as fire-worshipping.

Although I loved the festival, it meant hard work. Nana involved me in washing everything in the house: bedding, windows, walls, the expensive porcelain tea set trimmed with gold in the display cabinets in the drawing room, the cut glass candelabras and every single floor. I also had to scrub all the rugs and carpets with a wet cloth. I spent hours on my knees, until I ached all over, making sure they were spotless. While Nana mended all our clothes and some of our neighbours' too, Uncle Salman planted new trees and tidied up the back garden. As tradition required, we visited Baba's and Uncle Javan's graves to pay them our respects, before celebrations began in early March, four Tuesdays before *Novruz* itself.

Each Tuesday, called *Charshanba*, had a theme as we celebrated the awakening of water, fire, wind and earth. During the first *Charshanba* we honoured the purifying nature of water. Although the celebration on that day was modest, I still felt excited because it marked the ending of winter. The second *Charshanba* marked the awakening of fire with large bonfires in the street. Nana lit candles in the house to burn off any negative energy of the past year. By the time we marked the awakening of wind and air during the third *Charshanba*, the preparations for *Novruz* were in full swing and Nana bought chestnuts, walnuts, hazelnuts and even some pomegranates for the celebrations. The last *Charshanba*, which represented earth, was as big as *Novruz* itself. Tradition required that we had seven varieties of food on the table, and all of their names had to start with the letter 's' in Azerbaijani, such as sumakh, sour spice used with meat, and samani, wheatgrass Nana grew on plates as a symbol of fertility.

This *Novruz* was special, and everyone I knew made an extra effort to mark the day itself as it merited. Although Nana constantly complained about the shortage of money and the empty shops, she splurged on expensive produce to make *baklavas* in large tins – enough for our household, Mama's and Uncle Telman's. I watched as she alternated layers of thin pastry and crushed walnuts and hazelnuts mixed with sugar. Next, she poured honey and saffron syrup over the thick top layer and made cuts in the pastry to create diamond shapes. I decorated each diamond with a walnut and hazelnut halves. Of course, I did not leave the kitchen until I had eaten the first baklava of the season.

On the eve of *Novruz*, neighbours and relatives gathered around our oval table in the living room to make *shakarburas*. We filled sweet pastry with crushed walnuts and hazelnuts, sealed them on one side and, using tweezers, decorated the top with elaborate patterns. The comforting smell of *shakarburas* spreading through the house distracted me from the women's conversations about their relationships, the latest gossip and the current Soviet occupation.

On the 21st March, people's defiance of the regime drove them out into the streets to gather around bonfires, sing traditional folk songs and feel proud to be Azerbaijani. We were no longer individual families; that day we were a community. Even women were allowed to attend the gatherings. After a family dinner at home, I joined girls from the neighbouring houses who were flocking together around the fires. Someone on the other side of the flames started singing a folk song, his longing palpable, his voice sad. We all joined in with the refrain, pleading, 'please, look at me'.

'*There is a stone flying through your window,*
Please, look at me, please look at me.
There are tears in my eyes,
Please, look at me, please look at me.
If your family agrees to give you away to me,
Please, look at me, please look at me.
That would please everyone,
Please, look at me, please look at me'.

When the bonfires burned down to a manageable size, young boys, and even some girls, jumped over them. I waited tentatively before following them over the tame flames. The fire was supposed to burn all the negative energy trailing behind you, leaving you cleansed ready for the coming year.

I thought the scale of the celebration, a demonstration of our unity as a people, was awe inspiring. That night we all felt change was really coming. *Novruz* was bringing new beginnings for us and our country.

★★★

The first change for me was that Nana, worn out by her part in the *Novruz* celebrations, had decided to stay home the very next day. It seemed even she was feeling more hopeful now. She said she was thinking I was, perhaps, sensible enough to take care of myself.

'Let's see how you get on,' she said as she kissed me and went back to bed.

I thought I could easily prove my good sense to Nana. I was on the way home from school with Leyla again, freely reliving our experiences of *Novruz*, when we saw that the main road into the city centre was blocked.

There were no cars whizzing past at dangerously high speeds and honking at each other or us. The only time the roads had been free of cars recently was when people were pulling another Soviet monument apart and dragging its remains away along the still-named Lenin Avenue. This was before the Soviets had invaded the city.

As we scanned the street that day, however, we did not see a displaced statue as we expected, but a sea of solemn-faced people following a coffin, propped on eight men's shoulders. We waited, but the procession was so long, the crowd so dense, that we soon realised we could not cross the road. We decided to walk alongside it for a while and try to find out what was happening. We did not like to intrude on people's grief, so kept our ears peeled for any clues.

Then someone at the front started to chant: 'May you rest in peace, Javad Khan! May you never be disturbed again.'

Others quickly joined in. Their voices sounded more triumphant than sad, quite unlike any other burial procession we had ever seen. Then recollection tickled the back of my brain. I grabbed Leyla's sleeve and hissed: 'That's who used to own Mama's museum. Why are they burying him? He's been dead for decades, no, two centuries, I think. And why are they walking away from the Imanzadah?'

Leyla shrugged. No one said anything that explained it. The procession stopped in the Central Square, next to the

Shah Abbas Mosque, but we had to run, already late, to get our buses.

When I told Nana what I had seen she was surprised.

'No one round here has said anything. It's not been on the TV either.'

We had to wait until the next day to find out.

Asif knew all about it. He showed me an article in *The Voice of Ganja*, a local newspaper written by his mother. I was stunned to discover that the Soviet authorities had exhumed and reburied Javad Khan's remains several times since their regime was first established in Azerbaijan. Somehow, even though long dead, the last ruler of Ganja had posed a threat to the Soviet regime. Restoring his bones to his rightful grave sent a clear signal to Moscow that people wanted to reclaim their roots. The article described how the coffin was carried for two kilometres. Eighty thousand people attended the burial. I was surprised that the tanks had not run them over but then it was not technically a political demonstration.

Listening to Asif's enthusiastic speech, I realised there was no going back now. Black January had changed the attitudes of those who had tolerated, or even supported the Soviet regime. There was no chance of any reconciliation.

The chain of events following Black January added to fears of another threat to our freedom, even closer than Moscow.

16.

WAITING...

Ganja, Azerbaijan S.S.R., 1991

I was sitting safe behind the tall windows in the living room on a lazy Sunday morning, watching the snow falling slowly, when I heard a series of muffled but disconcerting sounds coming from outside. I opened one window a crack and pressed my ear to the frame's edge. There it was again, like someone was banging rapidly and repeatedly on a metal bucket with a poker. I stiffened in recognition. Was it a Kalashnikov? The beauty of the snow had not allowed me to forget for long. They were shooting again. The round of shots pierced the illusion of peace created by the floating snowflakes. The expectant silence of the in-between felt solid as lead. Then came a slower paced response, the unmistakable report of a shotgun, like the one Baba used to hunt with in the forests. His gun had been commandeered along with every other weapon in the city weeks before to be used by local young men who volunteered to fight the Armenians.

The lean-faced official had told us that the city needed every single gun, even rusty old ones like Baba's, to give to the volunteers.

'The Armenian forces are making steady progress towards Ganja. Now is not the time for sentiment.'

When Nana handed him the weapon, he thanked her with a curt but solemn bow, before marching off to the next house.

Baba's gun had killed many small animals. Sometimes when he did not have time to go hunting properly, he shot sparrows in the back garden. I remembered how my hands had got bloody placing the limp bodies into a large bowl. As I cradled my hot glass of tea that morning, I wondered how many people his gun would kill. The tea warmed my hands.

As I inhaled the comforting aroma of cloves that Nana always added to a winter brew, I relaxed for a moment. Then another volley of shots rang out: *Bang, bang, bang, bang…*

Was I imagining it or were they getting closer? A shiver ran down my spine. Nana walked in. Trying to hide my fear, I pulled the window shut and smiled at her.

'Would you like some more tea, Nana?' I said, reaching for the samovar.

'No, no, have yours, child,' she replied, settling heavily on her favourite wooden chair. It creaked under her weight. We sat in silence, me watching the snow, her watching me. I heard her sigh.

'They are approaching,' she said. 'I heard our troops are defending Chaykand.'

'Troops' seemed a funny way to refer to a group of citizens, mostly young, who alongside local villagers had volunteered to stand up, with limited ammunition, to the opposition's armaments, which included tanks. The Soviet

GULARA VINCENT

troops were staying out of the conflict and Azerbaijan did not have its own military force.

Nana's eyes were tired, empty of the fierce light that usually burned in them. Her lips were tightly pursed, pulling down the corners of her mouth.

'Oh Nana,' I exclaimed. My mouth suddenly dry, my tongue tasting metal not tea. 'Can't we escape to Baku?'

'I doubt we can. Two women alone. They took our only gun. Besides, everyone who can escape is doing so right now.' She sighed again then stared straight at me.

'I can't leave my home. It's all I have. And where would we go? Where could we go?'

I was shocked by her words. We had visited friends and family in Baku over the years. How about Minaya *Khala* with her three sons? I could name a few others. It was pointless to have a home if we ended up dead, I thought.

Nana seemed to read my mind. She shook her head.

'It's different when we visit Baku for a week or two. If we leave our home behind, we would be homeless.'

The word 'homeless' made me tremble. My mind raced for alternatives. We could not just sit here and wait.

I stood up, clenching my fists silently in frustration. I knew the truth, only Nana could make the decision, whether we fled or died. I was not supposed to resist or have my own opinions. Saving myself was not an option either. Girls were firmly under the wings of their families until they married in our world. If I left, I would be disowned and that, I had heard, was like a living death.

'But what shall we do, Nana?' It was the question I had asked many times. I expected her usual reply: 'Inshaalah Allah is on our side. Our men will conquer the Armenians.

They will never let them take over. Our city is the gem in this country's crown.'

I wanted her to repeat this mantra. I needed to hear it, but today she did not reply. She sat quietly, head bowed as if examining the patterns on the tablecloth.

I was suddenly irritated by her attitude.

'Nana, do you think the Armenians are going to win?' I said, controlling my voice.

It was all very well for her to just sit around. I reasoned since she was almost sixty, she was ready to die anyway, but I was young and was not ready to go without a fight.

Nana lifted her head and looked straight into my eyes.

'Gulush, you know that I love you.'

I did not know how to respond. Was this a statement or a question?

'Gulush, you are the light of my eyes. But if they come...' Her voice was husky and guarded. My insides churned, waiting for her to complete the sentence.

'If they come,' she repeated. 'If they come, I will kill you myself! They will not have you – your honour or your purity! They will not disfigure you in any way. Not my Gulush, my little...' She started to mumble to herself. I turned away. I could not take the words in.

Did she really mean it? Or was it like when she used to say, 'I'll kill you if you fail at school'? Could I resist her if she tried to kill me? Sometimes, when she was angry, I had found myself paralysed with fear. I had never imagined overpowering the woman who could pin me to the spot with her burning eyes.

Three rounds of shots exploded outside in the snow, even closer. We'd heard horror stories on the news – abused children, tongueless men, eyeless and broken women. This enemy did not take prisoners. They just wanted our land.

Although I did not know how I would survive, my impulse was to run away, but Nana caught me in her arms before I had even turned towards the door. She pressed my head to her chest. Her cotton apron smelt of fried onions.

'Even in death you will be pure and happy. When the time comes, you won't even know. Have no fear.'

As her claw-like fingers stroked my hair, as the sounds outside grew quieter, my internal questions grew louder. When she released me, I struggled to stay standing as she turned to the kitchen.

'Until then, we carry on. We can't let them win in our heads. Get on with your chores, I have cooking to do.'

As I went to fetch the dusting cloths, the questions ran faster round my head. How would she do it? Would she poison me, like Madame Bovary, in the book I had read? The gruesome details of her slow and painful death had made me shudder.

Shots were echoing more frequently through the blizzard now, but I kept polishing the glass of the display cabinets. I imagined them being smashed by the invaders. This thought led to questions. Would Nana just kill me, or kill herself as well? Would she slit my wrists, the way Mama had slit hers, all those years ago when Avaz's family had rejected her as his fiancée? The image of black rivers running down her fingers flashed in my head. What else could she do to me? Shoot me, perhaps? Was that why she had wanted to keep Baba's gun? I had seen blindfolded people put before a firing squad in war films.

As I remembered this, reality broke in again, as a stream of gunshots rang out close by. I nearly dropped the antique plate I was dusting.

At that moment, Nana came in, her face flushed from the heat of the kitchen, but as calm as a summer pond.

'You can leave that now. Come, sit down,' she said. Not knowing what else to do, I obeyed. 'Here you go.'

Nana placed a plate of meatballs, potatoes and chickpeas in front of me. I realised then that I must have been polishing the same cabinet for well over an hour.

I stared at my plate. The centre of the meatball would be a perfect hideaway for poison, suspicion whispered in my head. Nana usually called me to help with any cooking; 'chop those', 'pass that', 'pay attention', 'clean this', 'not that way'; but today she had not.

My appetite completely disappeared despite the smell of the food tickling my nose. Nana sat next me and started to eat her own meal. Her food looked exactly the same as mine.

'Eat up, it's good.' Then she smiled. 'Your brain is too large, Gulush. Don't worry, there is no poison in there,' she said. 'I wouldn't waste good meat like that now, would I?' She reached out her large soft hand and squeezed my forearm. 'I was upset,' she said, quietly. 'We all get upset, so dramatic in our family, sometimes. Aren't we? But listen, the guns have stopped. All will be well.'

Then she swapped the plates round.

'Gulush, eat your food. We need to be strong, us women, for what may come.'

The war in my head had become too intense to bear now. I wanted it to stop. I wanted things to be as they had been, so I lifted my spoon and began to eat. Within a few minutes, the taste and aroma had driven worry to the back of my mind.

★★★

Each day that passed became the same day, a mix of the ordinary and the bizarre. From when I woke, dry-mouthed in the morning, until I finally dropped into a fitful sleep at night, the questions ruled my head. Whether I was listening to gunshots echoing ever nearer, cleaning a carpet, chopping vegetables, or watching a movie on TV, they were always there.

How and when would Nana kill me? Would it be when the Armenians entered the city or when they were at the top of our street? No, that would not give her much time. What if they made it to the top of our street, she killed me and then our men finally won?

Nana did not talk about what she had said again. Perhaps it was the outburst of a tired and frightened older woman? I tried to believe that, but then I would catch her staring at me as I went about my chores. She would quickly look away. After so many years of having the importance of virtue, then later, the horrors of rape, pointed out to me, at home, at school and even on TV, I found such things all too easy to imagine. Could it really be worse than death, though? Did Nana know more about this than she had ever said? She should not have told me what she was thinking. I was already afraid of the Armenians invading. Now she had made me afraid of her, my own Nana.

In contrast to me, since that night, Nana had brightened

up. It seemed that by deciding what to do about me, sharing her fears, she had made herself feel better. She even hummed along to tunes on the radio and had started clearing out Baba's cupboard, untouched since his death.

Much as I loved her, much as I respected her, I could not shake off the questions in my head, even when our neighbour Amaliya arrived with news.

'Rosa *Khala*,' she shouted, as she puffed up the stairs. 'Turn your TV on! Quickly now!' She bustled into the living room and plonked herself, panting, on one of the best chairs. She sipped on her hot tea Nana poured for her from a large samovar. 'They've been forced back!'

'The Armenians?' Nana asked, banging the TV set, in a pointless attempt to speed its warming up.

'Who else?' Amaliya beamed, showing the gold in her teeth. 'Such good news! I am hot with the excitement of it all!' Her face was pink as a radish skin.

A blurry image of the news commentator came alive practically shouting about the victory. Nana and Amaliya seemed transformed, their faces lit up with smiles, whilst relief softened their previously hunched shoulders. How could they be so sure? The Armenians might come back in the night, like the Soviet tanks did after Black January.

'I always knew that we would win. This is a sacred land!' Nana declared, as Amaliya nodded her curly head like a puppet, and beamed.

I was frozen inside. I could not believe it. This speech, from the woman who only days before had talked about killing me to save my purity!

'What a relief! Isn't it, Gulush? We haven't slept soundly for days,' said Amaliya.

The two of them chatted away like little children, planning their celebrations and passing remarks on the announcer's outfit and the spectacle unfolding on the TV.

Soon I was able to slip away. Taking my coat from its peg in the hall, I quietly escaped into the front garden. The coil of anticipation that I had cradled in my belly for so long was still tight with betrayed trust. The cold air threatened to make ice crystals of my tears. I pulled my fur-edged hood in closer and sheltered from the wind in the lee of a wall. How could someone kill out of love? I watched, miserably, as a few cars drove past beeping their horns excitedly. Despite the snow and the thick glass windows, cooking smells were already wafting from every direction. Everyone, it seemed, was preparing for a party, except me.

If Nana noticed my mood, I was never sure, but she did seem to treat me more gently than usual for the next few days. For one thing, she let me finish a task she had given me before 'suggesting' the next one. Nana believed that the Devil would step in if you were ever idle, so she usually made sure I was not. Even when I had schoolwork to do, I was still expected to fetch and carry for her, rinse bedding under the cold tap in the back garden, hang washing on the line, iron it without leaving a single crease, as well as help keep all the rooms tidy, not just my own area.

After hours of rerunning events in my head, debating with myself, for I could never share this episode with Leyla, I decided I must put it behind me. It had to be as if it had never happened. Nana's may have been a twisted form of love, but it was all the love that I felt I had. However, I was never to forget the key lesson she had taught me, that my purity, my virginity, meant more than my life.

★★★

For us, the conflict did not stop straightaway. We would still hear distant gunfire from time to time. It was for many, me included, a struggle to relax. I wanted to know all the details. How far had the enemy forces been pushed away? How many people had died to achieve this victory? This anxious energy bubbled away in my stomach.

Nana's eyes may have brightened with the recent news, but to me it was but a glimmer of hope. The air still seemed saturated with fear as pungent as the smell of leftovers rotting in the kitchen bin. It clung to me, making it difficult to concentrate on anything else.

Although our city was saved, in other parts of the country warfare continued. The blood of young men was shed in vain as day after day we watched successive defeats on television. In Nagorno-Karabakh, whole towns and villages were lost. People were forced to run for their lives, abandoning their homes and possessions; something Nana would never have done. Some of them came to our city. When I saw them begging on the streets, some with missing limbs, others with their babies wrapped in rags, robbed of all dignity and security, I wondered whether Nana's way might have been a better one for them. What was life like without a home?

17.

IT WAS ALL A LIE!

Ganja, Azerbaijan, 1991-1992

While the dread of the war was hanging over the country, the start of the school year in September promised a return to welcome routines, for me. I practically ran to catch the bus that 1ˢᵗ of September, eager to escape the atmosphere at home. This was an extra special year as well, my last at school. I savoured my relative freedom as I waited at the bus stop. I would have sung as loudly as the birds above me if I'd been alone. I was impatient to see my classmates and gauge their reaction to the latest news that had stirred our household.

Two days earlier our government had declared its intention to become independent from the Soviet Union. My family's response, like that of our neighbours, was mixed. When I strode smiling into the kitchen to tell Nana, she got agitated.

'I didn't think you would be an idiotic idealist like your mama, Gulush. A stronger central government took care of small republics like ours. Independence?' She pursed her lips and wrinkled her nose as if sniffing something nasty. 'Bah, independence! It will cause more troubles than it remedies. If you leave a corpse unattended it will soil its own *kafan*!'

Mama, who was an active member of the opposition party, had a different view.

When I asked her, she beamed at me and launched into painting a different picture of the future.

'Now we will use our own resources. Now we can finally benefit from our own oil and gas. Now we can grow tea, cotton, grapes, lemons, pomegranates, apples – you name it – for our own consumption and not for the Russians.'

My classmates turned out to be of the same mind as Mama. Everyone seemed to compete in creating colourful images of the country's future. I wanted to believe them but many, though patriotic, sounded pompous and naïve. Nana's voice kept sounding alarm bells in my head.

A week after the start of the academic year, Ayaz Mutallibov, the President of Azerbaijan S.S.R., dissolved the Communist Party of Azerbaijan. He was elected as a president of independent Azerbaijan by 98.5% of the vote, with turnout reported to be 85.7% in single candidate national elections. From heated conversations at home, I gathered that figures quoted in the press were grossly inflated.

The news dominated chat in the school corridors, intensifying the nervous anticipation of change. Concentrating on any studies became practically impossible. It took only five weeks for the new president to follow through with Azerbaijan's intention to leave the USSR. On 18th October 1991, the Supreme Council of the country declared Azerbaijan independent.

The response of the population was still mixed. Some began to act as if the country was already free, whilst others doubted that Moscow was going to let us walk away peacefully. I was one of the latter, remembering the stealth of the Soviet tanks arriving in the night after Black January.

Much to my relief I was proved wrong. The transition to independence was largely peaceful. One frosty afternoon, 25th December 1991, came the news that the Soviet Premier Mikhail Gorbachev had simply resigned and declared the dissolution of the Union of Soviet Socialist Republics.

We, along with some neighbours, crowded round our TV set and watched, fascinated, as the red Soviet flag with a golden hammer, sickle and star, that had waved for so long above the Kremlin, was lowered and replaced by a tri-colour pre-revolution Russian flag with three equal horizontal fields of white, blue and red.

I stared at the new flag fluttering in the breeze, the people clapping and cheering in that faraway place that once was our ruler, and was surprised how lost and confused I felt. I was raised as a Soviet child, taught to value their systems and their customs in preference to my own. Images of taking part in parades, concerts and other events flooded my mind. I could still taste the sense of pride I had had in those achievements and academic awards. Was all that now worthless?

The Soviet Union was formally dissolved the next day. Nana was stupefied as if the world was ending. She cooked and tidied but seldom spoke. When Mama visited, she was as joyous as a spring lamb, whilst her brother, Uncle Salman, studied his precious map and debated with his friends if borders might change. To me, Azerbaijan seemed so small against the bulk of Russia, smaller than many of the other newly independent countries. Who would be our allies now?

***

Nana was sitting as close as she could to the gas fire, in the still-frosty living room, gazing glassy-eyed into its flickering blue to orange flames. It was as if she were trying to see into the future. I doubted any of her visions were positive ones. It was hard to even think of celebrating in her presence.

School was closed now for two weeks for winter holidays, but I desperately needed some reassurance and inspiration about the country's future.

When Mirza *Dayi*'s voice came again from our porch one evening, I perked up immediately, but Nana did not even move from her seat. She motioned for me to summon him upstairs. Her jaw was so tightly clenched she seemed unable to raise her voice.

'Cheer up, Rosa *Khala*! Accept the reality, the Soviet Union is gone. It is no more.' Mirza *Dayi*'s cheerful voice jarred with the hush of the house. 'This is the best New Year's gift. We have reclaimed our country, our future, our heritage.'

'I wish I could share your enthusiasm, Mirza. What about losing Nagorno-Karabakh. Haven't you heard news of Armenia's attacks?'

'What about them? Guns and troops, they had them. Where from? From the Soviets. They were experts at divide and rule. We are better off on our own without their backstabbing!'

An image of Uncle Salman's map sprung into my head. We were such a small country compared to Russia's vast expanse. Surely, we did not stand a chance if they decided to attack us directly, or indirectly through the Armenians? That thought never left me, as I paced round the house that holiday, doing chores for Nana, my mind constantly searching for some certainty in life.

★★★

Walking to school on the first day of spring term in January 1992, I watched how the world I knew was crumbling around me. The walls of streets were being stripped of familiar slogans from Lenin and Marx. There was a space on Central Square where Lenin's monument used to stand tall and proud. I kept thinking '*What would we believe in now?*'

I walked into my history class, my mind pre-occupied. Even the sight of my classmates did not cheer me up. The lively buzz of voices did not subside until our teacher, Aida Akhmedovna, raised her voice. She seemed strangely hesitant to speak.

'I know we've shared many history classes over the last five years. I tried to teach you, to inspire you…' She paused, gripping her handkerchief tightly.

I wondered if she was leaving. That would come as a welcome relief – she never inspired me.

'Perhaps some of you understood. Most of what I taught you was Soviet ideology. And, the fact is, I must tell you… much of it was, to put it simply, erm… not true.'

Several of us gasped at this. She took in a deep breath before continuing.

217

'The real history of Azerbaijan has been restored... You may as well forget what I taught you before!'

Suddenly everyone was talking at once, to themselves and to our teacher. What did she mean? Forget it all? Forget the five classes a week for five years? It was just weeks before our exams. What would we write in them?

Puzzled, shocked, angry or triumphant, their faces were animated, their conversation loud: but I could not decide what I thought. I had worked so, so hard to memorise all those facts of Soviet history, to make sense of them, even to excel in the knowledge of them. Now I was being told to erase them all from my mind, I felt strangely lost and hopeless.

'Come let us talk about current events together. What are your views?' Our teacher sat at her table, her head resting on her hand, waiting for our responses. To start with we were all quiet, used to being drilled in the thoughts of others, our superiors, but gradually class members started to offer up snippets of information, in a mosaic of sound.

'The Soviet troops are gone from the Nagorno-Karabakh now.'

'That means all barriers between us and Armenia are gone.'

'I think the situation in the conflict zone is uncontrollable.'

'President Mutallibov is determined to reclaim Nagorno-Karabakh with Turkey's support.'

'He's building the momentum to end the conflict using the military force.'

With all the arguments at home now raging round me at school, I sighed and shut my eyes. Too many voices to follow, too many changes and no way of predicting or controlling what came next – I had had enough of it all. How could I be expected to do well by my family, if even my teachers did not seem to know what they were doing?

★★★

As my final school exams approached, whilst I crammed my head with all the new 'facts' we had to learn, an alternative option to academia reared its head. Several suitors approached Nana asking, informally, if they could be considered as a match for me. To my great relief, she turned the first crop down; I was not ready at all, but worried that it would not be long before she found someone she did approve of.

The prospect of studying at university was slim because we had neither money for bribes nor connections to secure an admission. Once I left school I might well be stuck at home, working for Nana, eventually eager to agree to any marriage to rescue me.

Knowing my fears, in her usual well-meaning but know-it-all style, Leyla bombarded me with suggestions.

'Why don't you ask your nana to sell some carpets or jewellery to help you out?' she said, as we sat sharing a hot *pirozhki* from a newly opened private stall across from the school.

'She sold everything when Baba was ill, besides which, you know Nana, she won't pay for my university admission. If I were a boy, it would be a different story. It's pointless to talk about it. Let's face reality – university is not for people like me.'

Leyla frowned. I could tell she was not giving up that easily.

'My Dad can help,' she insisted. 'He says it's quite easy to get into Zoological Sciences. It's not his faculty, but he'll arrange it, I'm sure.'

I sighed.

'You don't understand, Leyla, even if your dad doesn't take a cut, the payment needed will be too high.'

Leyla pouted.

'But I can't imagine being a student without you by my side!'

I tried not to show my growing irritation with her. She kept replaying this conversation, but it would always end the same, in my embarrassment at having to explain the financial facts of life to someone who might soon be my ex-best friend if she did not stop going on about my situation.

★★★

'So, Gulush, what do you want to study at university?' Mama asked, stretching on a sofa in her one-bedroom flat, her face covered in a mask made of cottage cheese and egg yolk.

Not this again, I thought. She'd obviously had this in mind when she invited me round for a 'break from Nana'. Mama waited for my reply, her facial muscles stiff with the homemade gunk anyway. I would rather she had made an omelette with it. Was there any difference in her skin after she had used it? I felt the pressure building up and blurted out the first thing that came to my mind.

'I want to be a journalist like you.'

Keeping her face still, expressionless, she muttered: 'You need three articles to be published in a newspaper as a part of the admission requirements to the faculty of journalism. You'd better start writing something now. I can arrange for its publication in *The Voice of Ganja* at work.'

It sounded promising, but I knew nothing about the process and my shoulders hunched at the prospect.

'It's easy,' she reassured me, as she now beat the egg whites into fluffy peaks to mix with lemon juice for the next mask. She explained that I needed to pick a controversial topic and write something critical about it.

I shook my head in frustration. I could not think of anything. I hated the news then. It was always about our losses to the Armenians in Nagorno-Karabakh.

Shusha, Nagorno-Karabakh's capital, had been attacked by Armenian tanks and helicopters. Despite fierce resistance, with hundreds dying on both sides, the Azerbaijani forces had had to retreat. Fuelled by the loss of Shusha, Mutalibov had been overthrown by the Popular Front in Baku. The unrest caused had diverted attention and resources from the troops in Nagorno-Karabakh. Consequently, we had now also lost Lachin.

'Everyone's upset about Lachin, but I can't write about that, it's too, too raw.'

'Journalism is about writing the truth, however hard that is. You write well, Gulush, I think you could do it.' Mama sat, paused, her next mask mixed ready on her lap. This one would cling tighter to her face so she would not be able to speak at all. 'What do your school friends talk of?'

'Not much, mostly politics, boys and exams.' I squirmed, feeling cornered by her questions.

'Hmm. I see. Exams? What about them?'

'Just do your mask!'

Exasperated, I stalked to the bathroom to escape. As I sat listening to the dripping tap, an idea finally came – how to get a gold medal. I had been asking Tarana whether she thought she would get one just the other day.

I got to Mama just before she coated the area round her mouth with the goo she had prepared.

'Tell me more,' Mama said, after I'd blurted out my idea.

'As if you didn't know – unless a bribe is paid to the city council house, school director and relevant teachers, your grades get slashed. Girls like me don't stand a chance!'

Much as I loved Tarana, her confidence about getting gold had rattled me. A gold medal marked academic achievement and made university admission way easier; it was harder for the oral examination board to arbitrarily fail a candidate who excelled at school. To qualify, you had to have *pyatorkas* in all the subjects that you had studied in the final year. Based on my quarterly marks, I hit the targets, but the final exams could easily change that outcome. Rumour was that it was especially easy to meddle with the Russian language exam, as one 'rogue' comma here or there could easily reduce your mark to an undesirable *chetverka*, which could get you a silver medal at best.

'Perfect, write an article about that,' Mama said. She smiled then slapped the remaining mixture onto her chin, lay back and closed her eyes. I had been dismissed to watch TV or start writing.

Writing the article was hard. I knew what I wanted to say but the words on the page would not behave. I could not capture the right ones, but eventually I squeezed out two paragraphs and showed them to Mama as soon as her face was rinsed clean and blooming.

'It's a bit dry, Gulush. But leave it with me and I'll see what I can do.'

When I read the piece in the newspaper a couple of days later, I barely recognised it. She had transformed it into something much more exciting!

★★★

Although I studied diligently for my finals from May to early June, my nights were restless and sticky. I kept having nightmares about forgetting something obvious and failing.

My first two exams, algebra and geometry, were the ones I feared the most. I still remember the day I took them clearly. To pass would give me a passport to a new life, away from the confines of my home with Nana; to fail…? That spectre made my scalp as tense as steel. Pressing my arms to my body to hide half-moons of sweat, I sat at the back of the room waiting while the teacher handed out the exam booklets. The air in the exam room was stuffy and electric with everyone's tension. I rubbed my sweaty palms on my dark navy skirt before reaching out for my copy of the exam paper.

I read the questions then my mind blanked. No amount of massaging my temples helped. I slumped in my chair, panic building in my chest, shoulders hunched. Years of excellent marks were about to be for nothing. I was going to ruin my school career! I glanced towards Tarana, who was sitting in the second row ahead of me. She was about to prove herself cleverer than me after all.

To my surprise, I saw the maths teacher had paused next to her and passed her a mysterious extra piece of paper.

That was how it was done? I looked around. No one else seemed to have noticed, they were too intent on their own papers. As if feeling the weight of my stare, the teacher turned around, approached my table, and without a word slipped me a similar piece of paper.

I stared, in shock, at the folded scrap in front of me. Again, I felt the pressure to perform press down on my head. I hesitated momentarily then unfolded the paper. I did not ask for this, I said to myself. The teacher gave it to me freely. I picked up my pencil and quickly copied the answers faintly in the margin of my rough paper. As I finished the teacher swept past and lightly retrieved what she had given me. I never spoke to her, or anyone else, about it. Perhaps she had seen me looking at her, perhaps she wanted to give me an even chance? I would never know.

Over the course of two weeks, other exams followed one by one, with Russian language and literature exams being last. They were all uneventful, and I was reasonably confident that I had done well. After handing in my final exam papers, I headed towards the exit, relieved and slightly elated.

★★★

As I had predicted in my newspaper article, published weeks before my finals, I received *chetverka* in my Russian language essay. I qualified for a silver medal, but not for gold. The article did not help in any way; it only got me in trouble with the school director, who happened to be a member of the editorial board of the *Voice of Ganja*. For the first time in my school career, I was summoned to the school director's office to be grilled about my views on corruption in the education system. Suddenly, I regretted that Mama was so eloquent in articulating my thoughts on the subject. Jutting out his chin, in his smart grey suit, Chingiz Alekperovich sat at a large mahogany desk in his cosy office with elaborate bookshelves and expensive carpets, extolling the virtues of Soviet education. Lost for words, I nodded apologetically until he finished his lecture. I thought he would demand that I publish an official apology in the newspaper to say it was all a lie but, to my relief, he did not press me any further. I heard the warning loud and clear though: the school's reputation was not up for discussion in the press.

I did not tell anyone at home about my conversation with the school director, and when Mama pressed me to write another two articles to meet the admission criteria of the faculty of journalism, I made excuses and avoided her until she dropped the subject.

Two weeks after the finals, I received my transcript. Enclosed was an invitation to collect my silver medal from the school director. There was no formal ceremony – just a handshake and congratulations from Chingiz Alekperovich. From his passionate lecture weeks before, I knew that confronting him was pointless and pretending that I was content with a silver medal felt unbearable.

Despite my disappointment, the family was pleased

with my achievement and, every now and then, Nana nudged me to visit the school and collect my medal. I faked a smile for her and said I had to focus on my new priority: university admission exams.

I had no intention of going back.

18.

CHOICES

Baku, Azerbaijan, 1992

The article I wrote to help secure a place studying journalism was superseded by other events. The new president, Abulfaz Elchibay, worked tirelessly to reform corruption in the admissions system, bringing in a battery of written tests. Publication of an article was not one of the requirements, and my hope of getting into university was rekindled by his activities.

One hot June evening, Mama and I travelled to Baku. The bus felt like a heated tin and the open windows let in more heat, despite us waiting for the weather to cool down before setting off. I did not complain about the nausea and stiff limbs the cramped eight-hour journey entailed because I was savouring the prospect of applying to study at Baku State University.

We stayed at Nana's cousin's flat. Minaya *Khala* took one look at our worn-out faces when we arrived that night and led us to the kitchen. She fed us bread with cheese and chopped up tomatoes, then showed us the large hard mattress laid out for us on the floor of their second bedroom. Mama had a hushed conversation with Minaya in the kitchen, while I stretched out on the mattress, my eyelids heavy and drooping, wondering whether Minaya *Khala*'s three sons were already asleep. Her oldest son Ilgar was very stern. I had never felt brave enough to be friendly with him. Her second son Ilham was five years older than me. He was tall with soft features and pale skin. He looked like Uncle Telman and I liked him a lot. Her youngest son, Vugar, was barely two years older than me. He was young for his age and had often chaperoned me on trips out in the past. Being in his company did not feel charged or complicated.

I dropped off before Mama crawled under a thin sheet next to me and when I woke up the next morning, she was creeping out of the door in a floral dress.

'Where are you going?' I said, yawning. The flat was in semi-darkness.

'I have a meeting,' she said in a half whisper.

'What meeting? What about my admission paperwork?'

'Tomorrow, Gulush, we will go and do it first thing tomorrow morning, I promise. But now I have to go. I...' she hesitated, then came back and kissed me on the forehead. She was wearing bright red lipstick and her eyes were made up too. Her warm breath tickled my ear as she said: 'I am going to watch Elchibay's speech.'

I knew how much Mama adored Elchibay. He was a former Soviet dissident, a highly intellectual academic who had published dozens of monographs and articles on Oriental philosophy, history, literature and religion. Had her enthusiasm to accompany me to Baku really been because of politics? I felt disappointed.

'Can I come with you?' I whispered.

'No,' she straightened up and turned towards the door.

'But what am I going to do here all day?' I hissed. I sprang up to follow her. Although I loved visiting Minaya *Khala* and her sons, she was almost as protective of them as Nana was of me.

'Go for a walk with Ilham,' Mama said. She held me gently by the shoulders. 'You will be all right. I won't be gone that long.' She smiled. 'Now get back to sleep,' she turned me towards the mattress and, with another light kiss on my head and a swish of fabric, she was gone, closing the bedroom door firmly behind her.

I was keen on Ilham but knew many would say that spending time with a young man alone might ruin my future marriage prospects. The tradition was that I remained beyond reproach, innocent and pure in action and thought, until the right suitor appeared on our doorstep. However, I allowed myself to get lost in a fantasy of spending time alone with Ilham and soon dozed off.

The sound of running water in the bathroom and the whistle of the boiling kettle alerted me to the waking household. I stood up quickly, pulled on my blue cotton dress and folded the bedding in a stack at the side of the room. When the bathroom was empty, I spent ages styling my short hair.

'Breakfast is ready, come and eat,' Minaya *Khala* said as soon as I appeared in the kitchen doorway. Ilham beamed at me and pointed at a chair next to him. The small kitchenet with a cooker, fridge and two cupboards felt crowded even with just the three of us at a small rectangular table. I perched on my chair, intensely aware of his proximity as if his body were radiating a heatwave in my direction.

Avoiding his warm caramel eyes, I picked up a knife and spread butter on a slice of bread in what I thought was electrifying silence.

'Mama left early,' I said.

'Yes, I know, she told me she would last night,' replied Minaya *Khala*. I wondered whether Mama had also mentioned her suggestion that I could go for a walk with Ilham.

'Have Ilgar and Vugar left for work already?' I asked out of politeness, while Minaya *Khala* poured three large glasses of tea.

'Yes, Vugar is at work early today. And Ilgar is visiting his uncle in Mardakan,' Minaya *Khala* said, adding four teaspoons of sugar into her tea. Her round face was kind but worn out from hardship and struggle. She was widowed in her early forties and raising three sons on her own with practically no income had left tension and deep lines on her face. 'Gulush, what would you like to do today?'

I shrugged, then squirmed inside as Ilham's hand brushed against mine when he reached for the butter.

'I am free today, Mum,' Ilham said and I blushed trying to control my excitement. 'I could take our little 'village' guest and show her what a real city looks like.'

I heard the laughter in his voice but kept my eyes on my bread. Every time I arrived, he and Vugar would tease me like this. I could not stop myself rising to the bait.

'Ganja is not a village!'

'But do you have a subway? No!' I grimaced, as usual. 'And do you have a funicular? No again!'

My annoyance mingled with my excitement and now also curiosity.

'What's a fun-ic-cula?' I asked tersely.

'Aha. Got you there, haven't I? Clever Gulush doesn't know what a funicular is. Shall I take her there, Mum? For her "education"?'

'Well, I… Perhaps it would be a good idea. Sure, if Gulush would like.'

I was not sure what to say. She sounded a little uncertain, buttering her bread absent-mindedly while casting worried looks at me and then Ilham. We chewed on the cheap factory bread in silence for a moment. I knew I looked much less like a child than on our last visit, but it was well known that she prided herself on having brought up three hard-working, respectable and respectful sons. They did not drink or smoke or mix with unsuitable women. They earned their money honestly: Ilgar renovated flats, Ilham was a tailor and Vugar a TV repairman. Their family was poorer than ours, but generous with the little they had, and highly regarded by all.

I tried to keep my head down, my lips were twitching, but Ilham quizzically caught my eye as I reached for more bread.

'It sounds like it could be really interesting. I would like to see it,' my voice croaked.

After breakfast, trying to act composed and matter of fact, I waved goodbye to Minaya *Khala*, who stood, semi-frowning, at her window. In my mind I continued to justify the expedition. Ilham was my cousin, thrice removed, but he was practically a brother to me. His motives were purely educational. I needed to get used to travelling around the city because I might end up living here. However, despite all my logic, I noticed my skin was feeling sensitive where my cotton dress touched it and my senses were attuned to Ilham, strolling casually by my side.

'We are going to Baksovet metro station. Then we will walk to the funicular,' he said.

Our fingers entwined and I let my moist palm nestle inside his warm hand. I could not speak, overwhelmed with the sensation of skin on skin and the suddenly close fragrance of his aftershave. On the subway, I sat like a statue next to him. Crowds of people piled in and out at each station, but I barely noticed them. Ilham's thigh was pressed against mine. I felt sick with expectation.

When we finally left the carriage, I gulped in the stale, warm, underground air, trying to steady myself. A ride on an escalator lifted my spirits and distracted me from Ilham. Strangely, he did not tease me about my love of escalators. We did not have those in Ganja either! Once outside, the late June sun warmed my skin within a few minutes. Ilham took my hand and we started our walk. Since no one knew me in Baku, I felt comfortable holding his hand: doing the same in Ganja would have led to long rants from Nana or my uncles and possibly even bruises.

On the way, Ilham occasionally pointed at landmarks he thought might interest me. When we first saw the Caspian Sea, he promised we would go there after our mysterious 'fun-ni-culiar' ride.

When he said we were nearly there, I started to pull in front of him. I was genuinely excited, imaging something hi-tech, perhaps with a robot involved. I could not hide my disappointment when I realised we were about to board a mini train. Did Ilham still view me as a child? He laughed, as he paid the fare.

'Have some patience, Gulush! This is just the start of our journey.'

I sat on the front seat of the train, trying to still my right leg, which was tapping with impatience, a quirk I had inherited from Baba. The conductor joined the driver and we set off slowly, on the flat at first then suddenly, as the train started to tilt, I realised that a series of strong cables were about to pull us up a steep hill.

The funicular crept at a slow pace at a forty-five-degree angle. I wondered how safe we were as I gazed at the city view. The seafront, known as the boulevard, built in 1865 was framed with verdant trees, grand tall buildings boasting beautiful architecture and dotted with sparkling fountains. Countless multi-storeyed buildings sprawled as far into the distance as I could see. On my left, Baku fortress stood in its splendour with the Palace of the Shirvanshahs and the Maiden Tower, surrounded by thick walls built back in the 12th century.

'Beautiful, isn't it?' Ilham murmured.

My eyes sparkled as I nodded, silenced by the panorama. He was right! Perhaps I did 'live in a village', as he said. Too soon the funicular reached the top of the hill. The conductor carefully opened the carriage doors, one by one, and instructed us to alight. A breeze ruffled my hair out of place, and I surveyed my new surroundings.

'What is this place?' I asked Ilham.

'I'll show you.'

He led the way. He did not reach to touch my hand. We walked on in silence. I could not understand why he was suddenly so distant. The breeze grew stronger as we started on a narrow path with two rows of pine trees on each side.

I folded my arms across my chest protectively. The place felt exposed. Despite its beauty, it had a heavy, ominous atmosphere.

At the end of the path, a sheet of grey marble glistened in the sun. It was clearly some sort of monument, but I could not guess what, until we reached the end of the path. Then understanding dawned and heaviness descended on my shoulders as I looked down on the long row of graves in front of us.

I looked in both directions and was not able to see the end to the grey marble tombstones of that graveyard. With no need for words, Ilham and I paced slowly along the path, taking in the names of each person and their age on their death. They all had the same death date: the 20th of January 1990. I had heard of this place. This place was Martyrs Lane.

Tears came freely to me, as I remembered sitting with my family watching events unfold on the TV the day these valiant people stood up to the Soviet troops, here in Baku, and were so cruelly crushed by them with tanks and guns. Many who were laid here were disfigured beyond recognition, I knew that.

I remembered being with Nana, in the bazaar, when the men were collecting red carnations to commemorate the innocent blood shed in Baku. I remembered my fears; that the Soviet troops would barge into Ganja, that Mama would have to stand against them brandishing only a kitchen knife, that Nana would defend my honour by taking my life.

I could have ended up like one of these people. Any of us could have.

As if sensing my emotion, Ilham suddenly stopped and turned to face me. He put his arms round me and held me, my head cradled close to his heart, and waited until my tears stopped flowing. Nothing needed to be said.

The ride down was bittersweet. Breathtaking views competed with my thoughts. All trace of romantic excitement was crushed for me by the sombre memories. Ilham seemed similarly reflective.

'Let's go see the sea,' was all he said, as we stepped from the funicular.

By the shore, I raised my head to welcome the soft breeze from the Caspian Sea. The air smelt salty. I took in a deep calming breath. Small waves lapped at the edge of the sea front, where lines of trees provided welcome shade. We watched the water, the sky and the people passing by until a growl from my stomach reproachfully reminded me that we had not eaten since breakfast. Without being asked, Ilham headed for a nearby street vendor. I noticed he had to pick through his pockets to pay, so I hid my disappointment when he presented me with a cone of plain vanilla ice cream. My teeth struck small chunks of ice as I bit into it. It was locally and cheaply produced with generous portions of water instead of milk. I felt instantly frustrated that Mama had not thought to give me any money for my day out with Ilham.

I was determined not to go home early. I knew a few hours without food would not kill me. I had gone hungry many times before but thinking about that further dampened my mood.

Ilham's mood, however, seemed to have been brightened up by what was probably a rare treat for him.

'Have you ever been up the Maiden Tower?' He smiled a tooth-filled grin.

I could only manage to shake my head in reply.

'It's just over there,' he said, pointing.

Of course, I had learnt of the iconic 12th century tower of Baku from books and television. It looked far more imposing in real life, as it stood proudly at the edge of the old city bridging the ancient culture with the modern world. As we headed towards it, I wracked my brains trying to come up with a topic of conservation to distract from my hunger pangs, but then he took my hand, and again his closeness overwhelmed me with shyness.

Climbing up the narrow stairs of the tower in semi-darkness, I was acutely aware of Ilham's presence behind me. Was he looking at my backside? Was it too big? I had wanted him to go ahead of me, but he had insisted 'ladies first'. Now the stairs were too narrow, even if I pressed myself against the wall, for him to pass me.

'Do you know the legend of the Maiden Tower?' Ilham asked, panting ever so slightly as we reached a round room in the middle of our ascent. After a moment's hesitation, I shook my head, figuring it was probably a safe topic of conversation. To avoid his searching eyes, I surveyed the round chamber, which must have served as a living room in the past and contained some ancient carpets and pottery in display cabinets. It reminded me of the museum where Mama used to work. Ilham started climbing the next flight of stairs and I followed him.

'Apparently,' Ilham continued as he ascended, 'there was a young girl. She came from a wealthy family, but she had the misfortune of falling in love with a young poor man. Her dad forbade her to marry him and built this prison. Did you know that the Maiden Tower was once in the middle of the sea?'

'No,' I lied from behind him, concentrating on the steep stone steps.

'Her father built it in the middle of the sea to keep her there while he arranged for her wedding with an old rich guy. One day...' he paused to catch his breath as we reached another chamber, 'the young woman was in her chamber when she heard heavy male steps climbing up the stairs.'

The tower had only small windows, which let in little daylight, but as we stopped, I saw Ilham's face clearly. He was enjoying telling the story.

'She thought it was the old man who had come to take her away against her will. She ran up these very stairs to the top.' He illustrated this with a sudden burst of speed up the last of the steps. I rushed after him, smiling. He paused dramatically at the final archway for so long that I started getting impatient with him.

'So?'

'Oh, you are listening then, good.' He grinned and continued grandly. 'We are about to emerge at the top of the tower.'

As we stepped through the arch back into the daylight, I was dazzled by how high above the city we were on the one side, and the vivid blue of the Caspian Sea on the other. Ilham half-shouted above the buffeting of the wind.

'When she reached the top, she climbed over the parapet and jumped into the sea, never to be seen again!'

I could not help but sway with thinking of it. Ilham came in closer to me.

'But, little did she know, the footsteps were not her ugly, rich suitor, but her own true love who had swum all the way to the tower to reunite with her!'

We looked at the sea in silence. Did all love stories end in tragedy? What would I have done if I were that young girl? Would I agree to marry the rich old guy? Or would I rather die for my true love?

These were my silent thoughts as I traipsed unsteadily back down the stairs after Ilham. At the bottom, the smell of cooking kebabs coming from the nearby *Karvansaray*, the place where the traders rested, made me feel quite faint. I must have paled, because even Ilham noticed.

'Are you okay?' Ilham said.

'Yes, yes,' I mumbled. 'Can we go home?' I still felt I could not explain.

I was subdued all the way home, even the press of Ilham's thigh on the subway did not touch me. At the station, feeling a little dizzy, I was forced to grasp Ilham's arm for support. I think he mistakenly took it as a sign of affection and started to chat away again as we walked slowly along. Then I saw them, the berries.

They were small, round, yellow fruits on a tree at the side of the busy road, just in reach. I grasped a handful of them. The berries were covered in thick dust, but I did not care. I squished them into my mouth.

'What on earth are you doing?' said Ilham anxiously. 'You're not supposed to eat those. They're ornamental. They might be poisonous.'

I did not care. I fed myself another mouthful. I was shocked by the intensity of my desire. The berries were bitter, their flesh took the edge off my panic, but not my

238

compulsion. In that moment, feelings flooded me. I wanted to fill myself up. I was angry, angry about always having to struggle, always having to make do. I fought Ilham as he dragged me away from the trees, from the fruit that was delicious simply because it was my find. I was sure people were watching but I just wanted to eat.

Ilham, probably worried that he would get the blame if anything happened to me, made me spit the last mouthful out and 'tidy myself up' by threatening to walk me around the block until I did so.

'I don't understand you, Gulush,' he kept saying.

Even before we opened the door of the flat, some fifteen minutes later, my sore nostrils were being assaulted by the smell of food. Minaya *Khala* was cooking in the kitchen. I knew, as a guest, I would be expected to wait politely to be fed. Snacking between meals was frowned upon here, as at home. Still feeling light-headed I poked my head round the kitchen door and asked if I could help, hoping that might give me the chance to snaffle a piece of something.

The answer was a smile but a firm: 'No, my dear. You look tired. Go sit and wait.'

I could not settle. Even Mama's return did not help. Aware of Ilham's eyes on me, I took myself to the bathroom, until we were finally called to table.

I will always remember that meal: the white rice, the aubergines and onions sautéed in butter and the pickled green tomatoes: plain food, but on that day it all tasted like a feast. It expelled my nausea; it settled my stomach. Each spoonful added to an overwhelming sense of relief.

By the time tea was served with a bowl of cherry jam, my mind was free to think lucidly again. I feigned a headache and was allowed to go and rest. As I lay on the mattress, I could still hear Ilham babbling out an edited version of our 'adventurous' day. Part of me still whispered reminders of how I had enjoyed being close to him, how he had soothed my misery in the graveyard, but that voice was quickly obliterated by another. It shouted: 'I am done with poverty'! Reasoning like a young girl would, certain of my view, I stated firmly to myself: 'I am not willing to die for love! My life will not be a struggle or a tragedy! I will not compromise my future for someone who could not meet my basic needs'. Since my chances of getting to university were still so uncertain, perhaps marrying a rich man would be the only way I could escape my miserable existence?

★★★

The next day, Mama and I went to Baku State University. On the way, she told me about Elchibay's speech the day before, her eyes shining.

'It's as he promised, Gulush! All of it! He is championing the new law on education. No more oral examinations followed by arbitrary or partial decisions. No more putting bribes and connections above talent. This country will get the education system it needs to grow!'

She dabbed the corners of her eyes to stop her jubilant tears from messing up her make-up. I was aware people around us were listening, but her enthusiasm was infectious. Hope temporarily filled me up, as if I were a balloon. As we reached the Academy of Sciences metro station, however, the butterflies in my belly were back.

The path leading to the university was busy with people walking in the same direction as us. I spotted some nervous-looking faces, which no doubt mirrored my own. The grey multi-storeyed building looked very imposing.

The receptionist produced a list of courses I could apply for. Although the list was huge, choosing a course was not as difficult as I feared. Before we left for Baku, Nana had given me and Mama clear instructions. I had to apply only for courses I could study by correspondence because she could not afford to support me in Baku for five years of my study. There were only three such courses: Law, Russian Language and Literature, and Librarianship. Mama and I discarded two straight away. The Russian Language and Literature course was not likely to be as useful, now the Soviet Union had dissolved, and I could not imagine myself working quietly away as a librarian all my life. Without hesitation, Mama and I selected Law as my choice. If I were admitted, I knew that I could have two visits to Baku per year to sit my exams, with a lot of independent study at home.

★★★

We went back to Baku a month later, for me to sit the admission exams. I was relieved that this time we were to stay at Mama's old friend Zeynab's flat in Baku.

From the moment we boarded the train with her, I knew Nana would have hated Zeynab. She was everything that Nana disapproved of: her laugh was too loud, make-up thick, and her flowing black dress was above her knees, revealing long, tanned legs encased in stilettos.

While Zeynab went to the toilet and flirted with the train conductor in the corridor, Mama confided that her friend cheated on her husband, even though he treated her like a goddess.

'Their house is so grand, but once, when I visited, it was her husband who served us tea, on a tray, like a servant!'

Mama giggled at the shock on my face. She bent to whisper in my ear: 'Yes, really. But despite his devotion, she comes once or twice a month to Baku to see her lover, on the pretence of visiting her son.'

Mama stopped talking as soon as Zeynab sailed in, all smiles at the train conductor, who trailed after her carrying three teas, on a tray! I could not look at Mama. I tried not to let my thoughts show. I was not sure why Mama would have such a friend, but after a while of watching them together I realised why. Zeynab embodied everything Mama wanted in life: to be adored and free to be herself.

Staying in Zeynab's flat was not the experience I had expected. True, it was in a lovely neighbourhood and was modern, stylish, with a well-equipped kitchen, but it was even smaller than Minaya *Khala*'s flat. Zeynab rented it for her son. I was not happy to find he slept on a single bed and the three of us huddled on a large spare mattress on the floor in the same room. Mama slept in the middle, warmly wedged between me and Zeynab, who was nearest the wall. It was far from being the best place to sleep the night before an important exam. It was like when I had to sleep between Nana and Baba as a child, but worse. I teetered on the edge of the mattress, stock still, in case I woke anyone, or rolled onto the floor next to handsome but smug Jabbar's bed!

I was awake most of the night, which gave me plenty of

time to worry about the exam. It was the very first written admission examination to be held in Azerbaijan. Although all the fears I had had about getting into university without bribes or connections had been washed away by Elchibey's reforms, I was still very nervous. There were so many things I might forget, run out of time, or not understand the questions. My busy brain flashed vivid images of all the possibilities through my head.

★★★

'Eat this, Gulush.' Mama placed a slice of warm buttered bread in front of me, as we three sat at the table in the tiny kitchen the next morning. Jabbar was still snoring in the bedroom. Mama knew I always got tense and anxious about exams.

'At least drink some sweet tea, it'll help you to concentrate,' she urged.

'I know you will do so, so well,' said Zeynab. 'Your Mama has told me about all your achievements! Remember exams are just a chance to let people know how great you are!' She kissed me good luck and bustled out of the flat, to meet a 'friend'.

The examination venues were dotted across Baku and the admission tests were held in local primary schools. It took us forty minutes to locate the correct building, while my panic rose and subsided like the waves on the Caspian Sea. Despite all the stress and rushing, we were early. Too nervous to stray away, in case they called us in, we waited in the school courtyard.

I kept checking Mama's delicate watch and wondering

why no one had let us into the building yet. Were we in the wrong place? What if I was wasting precious time to answer my exam questions? I tugged at Mama's sleeve, demanding answers she did not have. Then I spied Tarana in the crowd. Her presence calmed me down. There was no way her mother would have missed the start of the exam. I waved but did not go across to her. I felt too tired and sick to socialise.

Eventually, a woman came out of the grey school building. She had to shout to get everyone's attention.

'The written tests are not ready. We are waiting for the paperwork from the central examination office. We'll call you in when they arrive.'

She disappeared back into the building without another word. All we could do was continue to wait. We had to wait another three hours.

Inevitably my stomach soon started rumbling. I tolerated Mama's 'I told you so' look with a silent pout. There was nowhere nearby that we could go to buy food and be sure to be back if we were suddenly called in. What made it worse was the smell of boiled sausages that wafted periodically across the main road from a workmen's cafeteria. Only men were allowed to sit outside to eat and drink. Watching them sitting there having tea and chatting, whilst we, a crowd of women and teens standing outside, triggered the uncomfortable memory of me, Ilham and the dusty, decorative berries.

By the time we were ushered to the examination room, I felt completely exhausted. Leaving Mama in the lobby, I was led, with all the others, into a huge room. Each one of us had our own small table, separated in rows. I flopped down and when instructed turned over the paper.

I had a range of questions in five subject matters to be addressed in the two-hour exam. I spotted Tarana's long braids a few tables ahead of me and wondered if anyone would slip her a piece of paper on this occasion. The English and Russian languages, literature and geography questions were fairly straightforward, and I ticked the boxes to answer multiple choice questions with reasonable confidence. The history section was by far the most complicated, but by the time I reached that section, my mouth tasted metallic and a headache was pumping a beat around my forehead. I answered the questions without bothering to worry whether I was giving the right answers or not. I just wanted to finish the exam as quickly as possible.

'There is nothing glamourous about admission exams,' I said to Mama, when I emerged from the examination hall, dragging my feet from exhaustion. 'If I get in, I hope that university life is more exciting than this.'

'And better organised,' added Mama. We both laughed at that.

19.

WHISKERS OF A TIGER

Ganja, Azerbaijan, 1992

S ince leaving school two months before, I had felt
isolated from the world outside our door. No friends
came to call, and I was not allowed to go out without
a good reason or a chaperone. Girls of marriageable age
seemed to need more protection than young children. I
felt sure that if I did not get into university or married off,
I would probably die of boredom.

Cooking with Nana was my sole entertainment. We
were making *gutabs* that day. I rolled the dough into thin
circles the size of a plate. Then she spread minced meat on
one half, folded the other half over the filling and sealed the
edges with her fingertips. Finally, she would fry them, two
at a time, in a large cast iron pan, until each side was a rich
golden brown, and pile them on a large plate.

I had to close the kitchen door to stop the frying fumes
from saturating the house, then fling open the door and
window into the garden. I paused, my head outside, to take
in cooling breaths. The smell of freshly turned and watered
earth filled my lungs. Opposite the door, two birds were
scrapping, shaking the silver leaves of our largest quince,

which stood sparkling in the rays of the summer sun. No rest for me, though. Nana's voice barked from the kitchen.

'Go get Amaliya, Gulush. If Mirza is there, say your old Nana needs help on a woman's matter. He'll never ask what. Let's treat her to surprise *gutabs*.'

I sighed but sloped out of the house into the sunshine without complaint. There was no point in that, this was my life, in limbo: the dutiful granddaughter. I crossed the dusty road, which seemed unable to stay surfaced, and opened Amaliya's tall, grey iron gate into a garden much like ours. She was sitting on a rickety wooden chair, chopping vegetables. Mirza, her husband, was dozing, his head lolling, on a bench next to her.

'Amaliya *Khala*, Nana needs your help with a woman's matter. Can you come, please?'

'Oh yes, of course,' she said, springing up with a warm smile.

Mirza barely stirred, as she pulled her galoshes on, her rosy cheeks flushed. She tried to tease out the type of help Nana had required, but I just shrugged enigmatically. She did not even guess from the cooking smells, until Nana removed the plate's cover.

'We thought you might like to help us out, with these!' Nana chuckled to see her face.

'Women's matters indeed!' Amaliya beamed with satisfaction as she bit into the warm *gutab*. 'Hmmm. Delicious! I wish you'd give me your recipe instead of saving it for Gulush. What will she want with it when she's a lawyer? This is timely. Not just because I was getting peckish...' She took a large bite and continued with her mouth full. 'Mirza is getting on my nerves again. We will have another fight when he finally wakes up.' Her words did not alarm me. Amaliya often talked about her fights with Mirza *Dayi*. 'Perhaps you could tell us one of your stories whilst we enjoy these gorgeous *gutabs* and some hot tea.'

'Of course.' Nana loved to be asked to tell a tale. 'Let me see. Yes, this one.' She smoothed her apron, as I poured the tea and selected my own *gutab*.

'There was once a lady called Fatima, who was famous for her loving relationship with her husband. Another woman, who had a terrible relationship with her husband, decided to find the good wife and beg her to reveal the secret to her happy marriage. After searching high and low, she found Fatima's house. To her utter surprise the 'good wife' was sitting out in the scorching sun knitting. By her side there was a broken jug of water and a piece of dry bread.

The seeker was puzzled. She wondered whether that was the secret she was after: Fatima's husband was no doubt working in the field with water and bread for lunch. After a moment of hesitation, she cleared her throat and asked: "Greetings, Fatima *Khala*, I have come to ask you an important question. Can you tell me what the secret of a happy marriage is?"

Fatima smiled. "Yes, of course, I will gladly tell you. But first, I have one condition. Before I reveal the secret, you must bring me the whiskers of a tiger!"

The woman shuddered. "Where will I find a tiger and how can I pull its whiskers out?"

"I don't know. It's my condition. If you value your marriage, you'll figure it out."

The woman left Fatima's house in deep thought. She wandered far and wide, even leaving her family to search for a tiger. Eventually, she met with a travelling circus who chanced to have a tiger as one of its exhibits. As luck would have it, the tiger's keeper had recently met with an accident, no one would say what. The owner was so desperate for a replacement keeper that he reluctantly agreed to employ the woman. Every day she would bring the caged animal some meat, offering it to him on a long-handled shovel, to lure him into the lockable end of his cage, so she could clean the other half.

As weeks and months went by, she reduced the distance between her and the tiger. They became fond of each other. She could see a sparkle in the tiger's eyes when she appeared exactly at the same time every day with a portion of the best meat she could buy. At long last, the tiger trusted her so much that she lightly plucked out a couple of his side whiskers without him noticing.

"Goodbye my friend," she said to the animal, as she gathered her belongings. "May blessings be on you." Then she travelled back to her hometown and rushed to Fatima's house.

"Here," she said triumphantly. "I have the tiger's whiskers, as you asked. Now, tell me the secret of a happy marriage at once!"

Fatima smiled and nodded her head wisely.

"Indeed, so you have, and the truth you have learnt yourself. When you start to treat your husband the way you treated your tiger, your marriage will become a happy one!'"

Amaliya snorted, whilst I sighed. It was not the ending

I had expected. I had hoped the tiger might turn out to be an enchanted prince or some such.

'I think we can all learn a lesson from this story,' concluded Nana grandly. 'Treat your husband reverently and he will have fewer reasons to be grumpy.'

'What about someone like me?' Amaliya protested. 'My husband doesn't treat me as respectfully as that tiger. When he gets his hands on some money, he spends it on other women!'

'You should have thought of that before marrying him,' Nana replied. 'A man who is unfaithful to one wife, is likely to treat the next one the same way.'

Amaliya blushed and looked down. We ate on in silence until Nana started another topic of conversation, as if nothing had happened. I knew not to comment and went to wash up.

As I put the kitchen to rights, I thought about Amaliya's plight. Nana said that she was paying the price for making a 'mistake': losing her virginity outside of a marriage. Somehow Mirza was never blamed for cheating on his first wife and seducing Amaliya. By not being a virgin on the wedding night, Amaliya on the other hand, Nana maintained, had lost 'both her bargaining power and everyone's respect'. If Mirza had refused to marry her, she would have been in a lot of trouble with her own family with practically no chance of leading an honest life. I secretly debated whether she would have been better off on her own than with her thankless husband, although I understood that at thirty-five years old, she had no chance of surviving as a single unemployed mum with no financial support from her own family and possibly Mirza.

As I dried up the plates and put them carefully away, I thought back to another afternoon, under the persimmon tree.

'How happy I am today!' Amaliya had said.

'What's happened?' I was curious. This was not like her.

'My men are fed and off to school and work. I've cleaned the house, done the laundry, prepared the meals and there is still time left to enjoy a cup of tea with you both!'

I had thought – surely that's not enough to make someone that happy? Didn't she have any dreams, aspirations and wishes, which went beyond mundane tasks?

I looked round the kitchen at my handiwork. All was gleaming and in its proper place, but I genuinely hoped that my life would not be like hers. I wanted more, a lot more than that, even though I had no idea what that might be.

As I took a fresh pot of tea into the garden, I heard Nana say: 'Enough of this talk. Let's have one more *gutab* each and you can take the rest home to your tiger, Amaliya. Don't take his weaknesses to heart. My husband didn't cheat on me, but he broke my ribs with a shovel when we had disagreements. None of them is perfect. But it takes a lot of strength and courage to preserve a marriage.'

I wondered whether I had enough stamina to survive such a marriage. In my heart, I knew the only way to delay any arrangements Nana might have in mind was my successful admission to Baku State University.

★★★

The precious results were due. My anticipation swelled like waves on the Caspian Sea. I paced the living room. What could I do? The TV. I flopped on the sofa. Channel surfing, I passed through news, a horror movie and settled on Sibel Jan singing a sad love song on Turkish TV. I tried to sink into the music and had just started to relax when the phone rang.

'Gulush!' The woman caller was crying.

'Hello. Mama?' A row of sobs answered. I was certain it was her. 'What's happened?'

There was something wrong with her, but what this time? Had she been fired? For once she was happy with her job at the local newspaper. She continued crying.

'Mama, what is it?'

Had she cut her wrists again and called to say goodbye?

'Mama, talk to me!' I raised my voice above her tears.

Silence: then she squeezed out a single word: 'Congratulations!'

'What are you on about?'

She took a deep breath. Her voice steadied a little.

'You. You are, you have… You've got a place at Baku State University. You passed the exam!'

It was my turn to be silenced, as the words sank in, then: 'What? How do you know? The results are not out yet.'

'I called in a favour with a friend and colleague who works at the *Kheberler* newspaper,' she said, much calmer now. 'My baby is a law student. All on her own, based on her knowledge. No bribes, no connections. It's almost unbelievable! I am so proud of you. One minute I laugh, the next minute I cry. I have never been so excited before in my whole life!'

She rambled on, alternating crying then cooing over me, until I heard someone calling her name.

'I've got to go just now, darling! But I'll come to see you later!' Then she was gone.

I put the receiver down. I had to process the news. Most of me believed her, but a tiny part of me doubted. They might have mixed me up with another girl with the same name. I hesitated to share the news with Nana. I decided to keep quiet and wait until I saw the results with my own eyes.

★★★

I greeted the next morning fully dressed, ready to run to the top of our street to buy a newspaper from a kiosk. When I arrived, the kiosk was still closed, so I watched other people loitering nearby for the same reason as me. When one boy's eyes met mine, I pretended to be studying our street's name plaque, filling my head with its history. Since independence, the street had been renamed. Instead of being a commemoration of an unknown Soviet hero, Chiragidzor, it now bore the name of Museyib Bagirov, an equally unknown Azerbaijani war veteran. I had looked him up in the school library: he was an Azerbaijani Red Army captain in World War II. He was awarded the title of a hero of the Soviet Union in 1944, after his squad killed 250 German soldiers and destroyed three tanks during the Battle of the Dnieper. I was probably the only person in the neighbourhood who had bothered to look him up. Most people did not even take the trouble to use the 'new' names. Lenin Avenue had survived on the lips of those he had supressed.

I was just daydreaming about how I would make sure any children I had would know all about their history when the newspaper van arrived. I rushed to the kiosk with the rest of them. I practically threw money at the seller, grabbed my copy and sprinted home.

At home, I lay the newspaper on the oval table in the living room and with shaking hands I started turning the pages. There were thousands of names in alphabetical order. After scanning several pages, I finally found my name.

'Nana, I'm admitted! I am in the Law Department,' I shouted, barging into the kitchen.

She stopped in her tracks, dropping a knife, which she was using to peel an onion, on the chopping board. Her face twitched; her colourless lips parted slightly. Tears appeared in her eyes then trickled down her wrinkled cheeks.

'Your Baba would have been so proud. It was his biggest dream for one of his children to study at university. May his spirit rejoice!'

She came around the table to embrace me and I crumpled onto her chest with tears of relief. I could hardly believe it. Only a few months ago I had thought I stood no chance of being admitted to a local agricultural institute, never mind the best university in the country.

'Gulush, this is a miracle! No one in our entire clan ever studied at university. I knew you could do it! You did it all by yourself.'

★★★

Seamlessly, a new page in my life as a university student began. Mama helped me to find a job at the local prosecutor's office and by September of 1992 my life had changed beyond recognition.

The streets of Baku were buzzing with cars and people running errands as I walked from the imposing building of Baku State University towards the The Academy of Sciences metro station to make my way to the flat of Uncle Telman's brother-in-law. Sevil's brother Azar, his wife and two daughters were perfect hosts during my study sessions. No one chaperoned me to and from university. Life was different here. People seemed to have different priorities and did not meddle in my life.

On the right side of the street, a row of newly opened private shops lured me in with their colourful displays. Most items were unique, mostly imported from Turkey and Iran. With the opening of borders with the neighbouring countries, new shops had sprung up, numerous as mushrooms in an autumn field, offering choices we did not have during the Soviet rule. Unsure what may sell, people who privately imported clothing from abroad hesitated to buy too many items. So, instead of rows of the same item in different sizes, the shops had tops, dresses, trousers and coats hanging on the walls all the way up to the ceiling to show off the colours and different designs. Small spaces were crammed with as many items as the sellers could fit in.

The smell of doner kebabs, wraps filled with sliced meats and salad, wafted from the open window of a café. I turned towards it and glimpsed a woman sitting by the window, smoking a cigarette, while sipping on a small cup of Turkish coffee. I fought an impulse to stare at her. Although women in my family smoked, they did it in secret, not sitting by a window in a public space.

I perused the colourful shops with a new determination: to own and wear a pair of trousers. In Ganja, I still had to wear long, ugly skirts. I could live with a knee or ankle length, but Nana insisted on the mid-calf ones. In Baku, with its two million cosmopolitan population, I finally had all the anonymity and freedom to wear whatever my heart desired.

With feigned confidence, I walked into the first shop after the smoking woman's café. My eyes scanned the displays until I spotted a pair of light blue jeans.

'Can I try those on?' I pointed to the ones I wanted.

While the young man fetched a long stick to unhook the trousers from off the wall, I looked around the shop. Nothing else grabbed my attention. I took the trousers into the changing room, a small corner of the shop surrounded with a thick, dusty curtain.

The trousers were big around my waist, but I liked their soft texture and how well they fitted my thighs. I twirled in front of the mirror, checking my backside. I knew I was unlikely to find their exact match in a smaller size even if I searched every shop in Baku. The waist might be too big, but I loved them. Besides, I knew I could only wear them in Baku for two weeks twice a year. I would have to hide them from Nana the rest of the time.

I took the trousers off, folded them neatly, reluctantly pulled my long navy skirt back on and walked to the counter.

'How much?'

'Twenty dollars,' he said.

Many independent clothes shops asked for dollars because the manat was unreliable and dollars were useful to buy goods abroad. I pulled a crisp twenty dollar note out of my closely guarded purse and placed it down on the counter with a smile. I had a strange pride in not haggling with him. He did not seem to mind.

The next morning, I put my new trousers on, drew a brown leather belt through the waistband loops and buckled it tightly. I threw on a loose black top, which easily covered the extra gathers. Now I was ready for my second day at Baku State University.

The windy streets of the city greeted me with their usual hustle and bustle, but I felt more at ease blending into the crowd in my first pair of trousers. My life was taking a turn that none of the women in my family could ever envision. It was the start of a journey for sure, but freedom was near!

ABOUT THE AUTHOR

Born in a small city of Azerbaijan during the rule of the all-powerful Soviet Union, Gulara was indoctrinated in a school system where bribes and corruption were the norm. Even though she was a gifted violin player, the only aspiration anyone had for her was that she should guard her chastity with her life and become a worthy wife.

The collapse of the Soviet Union and independence for Azerbaijan enabled her to apply for university on her own merits and gain a degree in Law from Baku State University and then a Masters' degree in International Law from The Western University in Baku. After some time working on legal education reforms for the American Bar Association in Azerbaijan, she was supported by the British Council in moving to the UK and undertaking her Masters' in European Law at the University of Birmingham. Gulara continued her studies in Birmingham by completing a Doctorate in Minority Rights. She went on to lecture at Birmingham University for fourteen years, where she remains as an Associate Lecturer.

She now lives in rural Devon, in the Dartmoor town of Ashburton, a single mum bringing up her two young children, attending to the love of her life, writing. When not writing, she works as an energy healer who supports women in recovering from trauma, so that they can transform their relationships.